Forensic Learning Series

CHILD MALTREATMENT

Assessment

Volume Three

Investigation, Care, and Prevention

Forensic Learning Series

STM **Learning,** Inc.

Leading Publisher of Scientific, Technical, and Medical Educational Resources
Saint Louis
www.stmlearning.com

STM **Learning,** Inc.

We've partnered with Copyright Clearance Center to make it easy for you to request permissions to reuse content from STM Learning, Inc.

With copyright.com, you can quickly and easily secure the permissions you want.

Simply follow these steps to get started:

— Visit **copyright.com** and enter the title, ISBN, or ISSN number of
  the publication you'd like to reuse and hit "Go."
— After finding the title you'd like, choose "Pay-Per-Use Options."
— Enter the publication year of the content you'd like to reuse.
— Scroll down the list to find the type of reuse you want to request.
— Select the corresponding bubble and click "Price & Order."
— Fill out any required information and follow the prompts to acquire
  the proper permissions to reuse the content that you'd like.

For questions about using the service on **copyright.com**, please contact:

Copyright Clearance Center
222 Rosewood Drive
Danvers, MA 01923
Phone: +1-(978) 750-8400
Fax: +1-(978) 750-4470

Additional requests can be sent directly to info@copyright.com.

CHILD MALTREATMENT

Assessment

Volume Three

Investigation, Care, and Prevention

Forensic Learning Series

Debra Esernio-Jenssen, MD, FAAP
Pediatric Specialist
Child Protective Medicine
Lehigh Valley Reilly Children's Hospital
Allentown, Pennsylvania

Ruchita Doshi, DO, FAAP
Pediatric Hospital Medicine Specialist
Child Protective Medicine
Lehigh Valley Reilly Children's Hospital
Allentown, Pennsylvania

Randell Alexander, MD, PhD
Professor of Pediatrics and Chief
Division of Child Protection and Forensic Pediatrics
Department of Pediatrics
University of Florida
Jacksonville, Florida

STM **Learning,** Inc.

Leading Publisher of Scientific, Technical, and Medical Educational Resources
Saint Louis
www.stmlearning.com

Publishers: Glenn E. Whaley and Marianne V. Whaley
Acquisitions Editor: Glenn E. Whaley
Graphic Design Director: Glenn E. Whaley
Graphic Designer: Connie H. C. Wang
Color Prepress Specialist: Kevin Tucker
Managing Editor: Holly Henry
Developmental Editor/Curriculum Developer: Olivia Sigmund
Associate Editor: Samantha Koester

Printed in the United States of America.

Publisher:
STM Learning, Inc.
Saint Louis, Missouri 63033
Phone: (314) 434-2424
http://www.stmlearning.com orders@stmlearning.com

Library of Congress Control Number: 2021923417
Names: Esernio-Jenssen, Debra, editor. | Doshi, Ruchita, editor. |
   Alexander, Randell, editor.
Title: Child maltreatment assessment / Debra Esernio-Jenssen, Ruchita
   Doshi, Randell Alexander.
Description: Saint Louis, Missouri : STM Learning, Inc., [2022] | Includes
   bibliographical references.
Identifiers: LCCN 2021050900 (print) | LCCN 2021050901 (ebook)
Subjects: MESH: Child Abuse | Emotional Abuse | Child
Classification: LCC HV6626.5 (print) | LCC HV6626.5 (ebook) | NLM WS
   350.8.A2 | DDC 362.76--dc23/eng/20211209
LC record available at https://lccn.loc.gov/2021050900
LC ebook record available at https://lccn.loc.gov/2021050901

Print ISBN: 9781878060358
eBook ISBN: 9781953119117

CONTRIBUTORS

Michael J. Marks
Chief of Police
Whitehall Township
Whitehall, Pennsylvania

Vincent J. Palusci, MD, MS, FAAP
Professor of Pediatrics
Grossman School of Medicine
New York University
New York, New York

Rachel Thomas, PhD, APRN
Advanced Practice Registered Nurse
Division of Child Protection and Forensic Pediatrics
Department of Pediatrics
University of Florida
Jacksonville, Florida

The Honorable Anna-Kristie Morffi Marks
Court of Common Pleas
Lehigh County
Allentown, Pennsylvania

Brian Allen, PsyD
Director of Mental Health Services
Center for the Protection of Children
Pennsylvania State University Children's Hospital
Associate Professor of Pediatrics
Associate Professor of Psychiatry and Behavioral Health
Pennsylvania State University College of Medicine
Hershey, Pennsylvania

Michelle P. Brown, PhD
Postdoctoral Fellow
Child Abuse Pediatrics
Pennsylvania State Milton S. Hershey Medical Center
Hershey, Pennsylvania

Elizabeth Riden, LCSW
Clinical Psychiatric Specialist
Center for the Protect of Children
Pennsylvania State Children's Hospital
Harrisburg, Pennsylvania

Chad E Shenk, PhD
Associate Professor
Department of Human Development and Family Studies
and Department of Pediatrics
Pennsylvania State University
University Park, Pennsylvania

Our Mission

To become the world leader in publishing and

information services on child abuse,

maltreatment, diseases, and domestic violence.

We seek to heighten awareness of these issues

and provide relevant information to

professionals and consumers.

FOREWORD

The child maltreatment field has evolved dramatically over the past 50 years, with each new innovation building on the contributions of professionals who have endeavored to create a better world for children. It is noteworthy that this assessment has been adapted from the work of one of the visionary leaders in the field of child maltreatment, Dr. David Chadwick. Everyone who reads and utilizes this valuable collection of work is benefitting from the expertise of not only the contributors to this assessment, but from Dr. Chadwick himself.

We must now view child maltreatment as more than a dedicated field of work to improve the lives of children; in a larger frame, the professionals working in this field are daily striving to improve the health and well-being of our world because the children we serve today will be those who shape the future generations. Thus, this incredible collection of knowledge and resources should be viewed more expansively as a blueprint for achieving this broader goal, with guidance from wise and esteemed leaders in the field.

The multidisciplinary response to child maltreatment and awareness of the valuable contributions made by each of these disciplines is critical for an effective response to child maltreatment. Initial multidisciplinary efforts involved a limited number of professions, but we are now in an era where additional professional fields are becoming involved in the expanding response to child maltreatment. This assessment volume includes emerging topics of dramatic importance for those working in the child maltreatment field and builds on the existing knowledge and practice base to assist professionals in their effectiveness while working with abused and neglected children.

Furthermore, the child maltreatment field, buoyed by the continued revision of this valuable information, has been propelled from a practice of best efforts to a more evidence-based and evidence-informed practice, thereby leading to better outcomes for children and our society as a whole. Aside from being an outstanding compilation of knowledge related to child maltreatment prevention and intervention, this assessment also serves as a motivator for readers to promote improved practice and further evolution of the entire field.

The multidisciplinary response and value is not measured in comparison to each involved discipline. It is measured in the combined positive impact that this collaboration has for each child and family served. This *Child Maltreatment Assessment, Volume 3: Investigation, Care, and Prevention* provides the necessary guidance for allied professionals to provide their services in the most effective manner while also increasing their understanding of their multidisciplinary partners. This approach will continue to bring the change desired by all those who accept the challenge of child protection and well-being.

Chris Newlin, MS, LPC
Executive Director
National Children's Advocacy Center
Huntsville, Alabama

PREFACE

Identifying child abuse is only the first step toward child protection. A century and a half ago in the United States, specific laws did not exist to protect children, but as awareness of extreme cases of child abuse grew, organizations developed and began to advocate for the protection and rights of children. Internationally, the United Nations Convention on the Rights of the Child codified a legally-binding international agreement setting out the political, economic, civil, social, and cultural rights of every child, regardless of their race, religion, or abilities. As of today, 63 countries have legally banned any kind of corporal punishment of children. Despite these international developments, the United States and several other countries have not yet adopted these formal protections.

Today, law enforcement, medical examiners and coroners (ME/Cs), social workers, lawyers, and other professionals work together to more effectively prevent, identify, treat, and prosecute in citations of child maltreatment. Law enforcement has become increasingly proficient in understanding child abuse and working with other professionals to investigate and charge perpetrators. While social media has created a major avenue to better understand the sequence of events and often the motivation that leads to a specific episode of child abuse, the internet also creates opportunities for abuse – cyber bullying, distribution of child pornography, and more advanced ways to engage in human trafficking. Alongside health care workers, such as child abuse pediatricians, ME/Cs use DNA and other techniques to allow for determination in some cases that could not be done before. ME/Cs and law enforcement officials cooperate in preserving scenes, re-enactments, and trying to solve the specifics of cases.

Although most child abuse cases reported to the state hotlines are handled by social workers, others are seen in juvenile court and are sometimes considered criminal matters. Child death review teams, made up of health care professionals, ME/Cs, law enforcement, social workers, and legal professionals, are brought together for court cases, so precise and consistent written and photographic documentation aid tremendously in determining the ruling in court cases. In addition, these professionals may be called upon to testify, communicating the information within the confines of the legal process itself. Lawyers and courts make decisions in child abuse cases that will impact the child and family for years to come.

An entire system has evolved to address child abuse and achieve the best outcomes of an often negative situation. Although prevention is preferred, until that proves overwhelmingly effective, professionals need evidence-based resources to learn the best methods for intervention. With this assessment, professionals will gain knowledge about dealing with child abuse and its aftermath.

Debra Esernio-Jenssen, MD, FAAP
Ruchita Doshi, DO, FAAP
Randell Alexander, MD, PhD

REVIEWS

The occurrence of child maltreatment remains a pervasive public health challenge. Often, children remain as "invisible victims" who live in the shadow of their abuse and neglect. As such, it is imperative for clinicians to understand the foundational facets of targeted and sensitive assessment, as well as appropriate intervention and referral. Children, as they rapidly move through growth and development, require the clinician to provide trauma related care that is age appropriate and that promotes on time bio-psycho-social progression. This textbook provides a multidimensional and interdisciplinary approach toward increased awareness, expanded assessment, and recommendations for treatment for this very vulnerable population of children. Additionally, the strategic use of case studies in the Photographic Atlas section provides for the ability of the reader to immediately translate the provided information toward enhancing safe and effective clinical practice. Child Maltreatment Assessment: Investigation, Care, and Prevention *provides a solid foundational overview of the significant facets of assessment along the continuum of identification of child abuse and implementation of related strategies for safety and integration of the trauma. This is an excellent addition to any clinician's library of resources.*

Paul Thomas Clements, PhD, RN,
ANEF, DF-AFN
Professor in Residence
University of Nevada, Las Vegas
Distinguished Fellow, Academy of
Forensic Nursing

This text provides thorough, start-to-finish approaches for all professionals that work with children who have experienced maltreatment. It is clear that Drs. Esernio-Jenssen, Alexander, and Doshi intentionally set the stage for authors to present traditional and novel evidence-based information related to the etiology, prevention, treatment, and reporting of various types of abuse. These authors comprehensively consider the short- and long-term effects of maltreatment, including what we now know about the neurobiology of trauma, all while addressing strategies to provide patient- and family-centered care. In addition, and unique to this text, chapters provide case studies and photographs for discussion that clearly depict authentic situations and lead to deeper understandings of realistic practice implications. This assessment is a must-read for all who aim to remedy the epidemic of child maltreatment!

Sara Jones, PhD, APRN, PMHNP-BC,
FAAN, FAANP

The *Child Maltreatment Assessment series, a new 3-volume-workbook series should be a welcomed addition to both individual and institutional libraries as an authoritarian compendium that promises to be an invaluable resource for health care professionals as well as the disciplines of child protection, mental health, and law enforcement. The chapters that I had the pleasure of reviewing were thorough, well-written, and provided an easy-to-understand overview of complicated topical issues. The integration of a case-based format should in turn be of great practical value to the reader. There should be little doubt that the distinguished editors, Drs. Debra Esernio-Jenssen, Randell Alexander, and Ruchita Doshi have artfully selected both traditional and emerging topics contributed by well recognized authorities in the field. I look forward to adding this text to my library.*

Martin A. Finkel, DO, FAAP
Professor of Pediatrics
Child Abuse Research Education &
Service (CARES) Institute
Rowan University
Glassboro, New Jersey

CONTENTS IN BRIEF

CONTENTS IN DETAIL

◆

CHILD MALTREATMENT

Assessment

Volume Three

Investigation, Care, and Prevention

Forensic Learning Series

STM **Learning,** Inc.

Leading Publisher of Scientific, Technical, and Medical Educational Resources
Saint Louis
www.stmlearning.com

Section

I

DEFINITIONS

OBJECTIVES

After reviewing this section, the reader will be able to:

1. *Clearly identify and define key terms related to child maltreatment.*

2. *Accurately apply terms when analyzing cases of child maltreatment.*

INSTRUCTIONS

The following terms are found throughout the text. This section should serve as a convenient reference for readers as they move through the chapters.

— ***Accomplice:*** A person who knowingly, voluntarily, or intentionally gives assistance to another in the commission of a crime. An accomplice is criminally liable to the same extent as the principal and is typically present when the crime is committed.

— ***Cause of Death:*** The disease or injury that creates the physiologic disturbance that leads to death.

— ***Chain-of-Custody Log:*** Chronological documentation (ie, paper trail) that records the sequence of custody, control, transfer, analysis, and disposition of physical and/or electronic evidence.

— ***Child Fatality Review Teams (CFRs):*** A multidisciplinary group that assists with the proper identification of the causes of child deaths. In doing so, they gain a better understanding of the risk factors and circumstances surrounding the death, enabling them to design community and organizational interventions aimed at preventing future deaths.

— ***Child Protective Services (CPS):*** The government agency responsible for protecting children, which includes intervening in cases of maltreatment.

— ***Circumstantial Evidence:*** Evidence that is not based on personal knowledge or observations of a crime; deductions are made about particular facts, indirectly proving that certain events took place.

— ***Competency:*** Cross examination ploy; meant to allege a witness's lack of experience or certification in a variety of disciplines and/or point out a mistake or false statement given by the witness regarding their profession.

— ***Coroner:*** An elected official, not usually a physician, who is responsible for overseeing the details related to a death, including the maintenance of the body and preservation of any forensic evidence.

— ***Cross Examination:*** In a court of law, this is the interrogation of a witness from the other party of the case in order to challenge or extend the testimony already given. There are 5 cross examination ploys.

— ***Defendant:*** The person being accused of a crime or injustice in a legal case.

— **Defense:** The evidence and arguments that are presented in support of the defendant's opposition to their charges.

— **Demonstrative Evidence:** Consists of things (eg, photographs, medical illustrations, x-rays, etc.) rather than the assertions made by witnesses about said things.

— **Deposition:** The process of giving sworn evidence in a legal case (eg, a witness's written statement describing an event).

— **Dialectical Behavior Therapy for Adolescents (DBT-A):** An adaptation of DBT that is appropriate for children aged 12 to 18 years with presenting concerns related to suicidal ideation, suicide attempts, non-suicidal self-injury, or chronic emotion dysregulation, including those with a history of child maltreatment.

— **Differential Diagnosis:** The process of differentiating between 2 or more conditions which share similar signs and symptoms.

— **Direct Evidence:** Evidence that directly links a person to a crime with no need for inference.

— **Discovery Deposition:** Taken to discover information; helps to determine what the proposed testimony may be.

— **Evidence-Based Treatments (EBTs):** Treatment methods backed by scientific research. The majority of EBTs are derived from the cognitive and behavioral fields.

— **Evidentiary Deposition:** When a deposition (transcribed or video) is taken to be used in court instead of the live witness. This can occur when the witness will be unavailable at the time of the trial (eg, out of the country).

— **Expert Witness:** An individual who knows more than the average person, thereby giving them the ability to assist the jury or judge (ie, virtually all doctors). They can supply opinions about what the facts mean.

— **Exploitation:** The unfair use of something/someone for one's own advantage. In the context of child maltreatment, the term refers to the use of children to perform physical labor or sexual acts, either for profit or the perpetrator's personal gratification.

— **Fact Witness:** Someone who merely describes what happened (eg, "that is my signature") and supplies no opinion.

— **Gradual Exposure:** Meant to desensitize children to reminders, memories, and physical stimuli associated with abusive experiences; done by encouraging the child, through carefully calibrated increments, to talk and write about increasingly upsetting aspects of their trauma.

— **Hearsay:** Secondhand information made by out-of-court declarants whose statements were not made under oath and whose credibility cannot be evaluated by the jury; typically inadmissible in a judicial proceeding.

— **Hostility:** Cross examination ploy; meant to upset the witness and diminish the testimony by getting the witness to respond in an inappropriate display of anger or fear.

— **Inconsistencies:** Cross examination ploy; meant to point out any possible inconsistencies in a given testimony thereby impeaching it by displaying a lack of credibility.

— *Interrogation:* Formal or repetitive questioning, usually by a member of law enforcement.

— *Interview:* The process of one person obtaining information from another by a question-and-answer method.

— *Law of Evidence:* System of rules and standards that regulates the admission of proof in a court proceeding.

— *Litigation:* The process by which legal action is taken (ie, going to court).

— *Manner of Death:* Describes how the cause of death occurred. Manners of death include natural, accident, suicide, homicide, and undetermined.

— *Medical Examiner:* Board-certified physician with in-depth training in anatomy, physiology, medicine, and forensic pathology. They conduct detailed autopsies and scene investigations and determine the cause and manner of death in unexplained circumstances.

— *Miranda Rights:* Specific legal rights that are either read aloud or written by a law enforcement agent to anyone being taken into custody. A law enforcement agent's failure to give these rights to a suspect can make any of the suspect's statements inadmissible in court.

— *Neglect:* The omission of care by a parent or guardian, resulting in harm or potential harm to a child. Neglect is the most common form of child maltreatment.

— *Non-Directive Play Theory:* Also known as *Child-Centered Play Theory*, a humanistic treatment focused on the development of rapport. The therapist focuses on providing a safe environment where the child can express their thoughts and feelings without judgment. The child is free to play however they choose, and the therapist then provides reflective and supportive comments. Over time, the child will begin to feel accepted, hypothetically resulting in an increase of self-esteem and decrease in psychiatric problems.

— *Parens Patriae:* Legal protector of citizens unable to protect themselves.

— *Parent-Child Interaction Therapy (PCIT):* An evidence-based parenting intervention for children aged 2 to 7 years (there is an adapted version for children aged between 8 to 12 years). The PCIT model provides live coaching to caregivers, helping them interact with their child in a way that gives praise, focuses on desired behaviors, and teaches age-appropriate rewards and consequences.

— *Perpetrator:* Someone who commits an illegal or harmful act.

— *Plaintiff:* In civil cases, the person or party who is seeking legal action for something that they have deemed unjust.

— *Present Sense Impressions:* Statements describing or explaining an event or condition that are made while the declarant was perceiving the event or condition immediately thereafter.

— *Prevention:* Refers to the methods by which there is an attempt to lower the rates of child maltreatment.

— *Primary Prevention:* Efforts aimed at the general population for the purpose of keeping maltreatment from happening; the taking of action before child maltreatment has occurred to prevent it from happening.

— *Prosecution:* The side of a legal case that presents evidence and argues for the guilt of the person that was accused of a crime.

— *Psychoanalytic Play Theory:* In this model of treatment, the child is allowed to choose play materials (eg, a sand tray) and the clinician then attempts to interpret the likely symbolic meaning of the child's observable play. Hypothetically, when a child becomes aware of what their play represents in the unconscious, it will then help the child to more readily express their thoughts and feelings consciously, thus beginning the process of healing.

— *Randomized Clinical Trials (RCTs):* Well-controlled trials that determine the best method of treatment. The results of RCTs clearly demonstrate that some approaches yield greater benefits than others for the treatment of specific conditions.

— *Secondary Prevention:* Efforts aimed at a particular group with increased risk in an attempt to prevent maltreatment from happening; intervening right after child maltreatment has occurred.

— *Subpoena:* Requires someone to make an appearance in court or provide evidence for a case.

— *Sudden Unexpected Infant Death (SUID):* Also known as *sudden infant death syndrome* or *sleep-related infant death*, describes the quick and unexpected death of an infant (child less than 1 year of age), typically while sleeping.

— *TEN-4 FACESp:* A tool that is used to identify suspicious bruising. It stands for **T**orso (chest, abdomen, back, genitourinary area), **E**ars, **N**eck, **4** months or younger in age, **F**renulum (bruising and/or tearing), **A**ngle of the jaw, **C**heek, **E**yes, **S**clera, and **p**atterned bruising.

— *Tertiary Prevention:* Efforts aimed at inhibiting the further maltreatment of those who have already been victimized; working over a period of time to change conditions in the environments that promote or support child maltreatment.

— *Trauma-Focused Cognitive-Behavioral Therapy (TF-CBT):* The most well-established EBT for reducing post-traumatic stress disorder symptoms and other mental health sequelae in children who have experienced various types of trauma, including maltreatment. Its 3 primary phases include skill development, trauma narration and processing, and real-world mastery.

— *Two-in-One:* Cross examination ploy; meant to make a statement and then ask a question or 2; the statement is usually negative regarding you or your given testimony.

— *Witness:* A person with first-hand knowledge of an event that testifies to that knowledge during a trial or other legal proceeding.

Section

INFORMATIONAL CHAPTERS

The Role of Law Enforcement in the Investigation of Child Maltreatment

Michael J. Marks

Objectives

After reviewing this chapter, the reader will be able to:

1. Understand the role of law enforcement personnel in child abuse cases.

2. Describe why children are often the target of maltreatment.

3. Outline the 8 general steps for law enforcement personnel to follow while conducting an interview.

4. List sample questions to use when establishing rapport with the child.

5. Understand the basic information that should be obtained from a witness while interviewing them.

6. Understand how to use a preliminary investigative checklist to structure a case's approach.

7. Describe the procedures that should be followed at a crime or event scene.

Law Enforcement and the Child Victim

The abuse, neglect, and exploitation of children are all crimes, and while police officers report and investigate them, this is only a small portion of law enforcement's overall responsibilities. Other than in the largest police departments, there are very few police officers that are solely dedicated to the investigation of crimes against children. For the vast majority of police departments, the lack of specialized training, coupled with a general lack of experience in these very difficult and complicated cases, contributes to the difficulty in proving or disproving the allegations or suspicions of child maltreatment.

Police officers swear an oath to protect and serve their jurisdiction and these young victims need the investigators and prosecutors to serve as their voice when they are the victims of heinous crimes. These investigations require dedication, desire, and the ability to easily talk to both adults and children. Communication is the key to successful investigations and listening opens the door to many of the facts that are pertinent to the case.

All investigations begin with a suspicion or allegation. The majority of reports of crimes to police departments are by victims who are eager to provide details and information. Crimes against children, however, are considerably different. The report or disclosure of the event is seldom deliberate. In most cases, children do not report being abused. Depending on the child's age and developmental level, they may not understand what has happened to them or that they have been abused. The investigation of child abuse is one of the most difficult cases handled by law enforcement agencies due to the following reasons:

— Because of their physical, mental, and emotional development, children are usually unable to protect themselves from abuse, neglect, and exploitation.

— These crimes are often conducted in a private place, one-on-one, so there are no witnesses and no accomplices.

— Defendants in these cases do not usually brag about their crimes, so it is unlikely that a third party will report them.

— Children can sometimes be viewed as less credible or competent than the suspected adult offender.

— Interviewing children requires special training, understanding, and patience.

— Children often do not speak about their abuse for a variety of reasons. In some cases, the disclosure is delayed or delivered piecemeal over an extended period of time.

— Children often do not want the offender punished; they often only want the abuse to stop.

— Most crimes against children are not isolated incidents; they take place over a period of time and may involve multiple victims and even multiple offenders.

— Crimes of abuse may have no physical or medical evidence. If such evidence does exist, it does not necessarily prove who the suspect is.

— Cases often cross jurisdictional and political boundaries, making the determination of a venue difficult.

— The criminal justice system was not designed with the special needs of children taken into consideration; therefore, children may be frightened and/or intimidated by the courtroom and trial process.

— Child maltreatment crimes are often investigated by persons who have little specialized training or experience in dealing with children's traumatic events.

— Child maltreatment cases often involve concurrent civil, criminal, and sometimes administrative investigations that result in investigative conflicts and obstructions.

INTERVIEW GUIDELINES

It is important to gather all available case and background information prior to the conduction of an interview. An ***interview***, by definition, is the process of one person obtaining information from another by a question-and-answer method. Along with gathering information prior to the interview, the investigator may visit the scene of the reported crime, if pertinent to the case itself. The investigator should also make sure that they understand the offense and the events of the crime. It is important for the investigator to speak with medical personnel and ensure their competency regarding the manner and cause of injuries. Remember, neither guilt nor innocence should be assumed. Every incident should be evaluated and investigated on its own merit.

The following should be documented while conducting an individual's interview:

— Correct spelling of their name

— Date of birth and Social Security number

— Home address, including apartment number, floor, and location (eg, front or rear)

— Telephone number, specifically a cell phone and work phone number

— Secondary contact person's name, address, cell phone number, and work phone number

Be sure to conduct the interview away from other victims, witnesses, or suspected perpetrators. Select a site is that is convenient and familiar to the victim, a neutral setting, or, in the case of a child interview, select a place that is child-friendly and private. Conduct the interview as soon as possible after the event has occurred so that the witnesses' statements are not affected by memory loss or by talking to others. Additionally, a child forensic interview specialist should be utilized in the cases where an interview of a child is to occur. For all other interviews, the lead investigator should conduct them, if possible. While interviewing, communicate thoughts clearly and accurately, avoiding any display of bias in nonverbal communication, and remain professional at all times.

Interview questions should be focused on the injury or incident being investigated, keeping in mind the alleged offense. In formulating questions, make sure that they are:

— Short, clear, and easily understood

— Confined to 1 topic at a time

— Not confined to "yes" or "no" answers

— Not leading questions (eg, beginning with "did" or "does")

— Comparison-type questions when you want to pinpoint details

There are 8 steps to conducting an interview, although an interview should be tailored to each individual and specific situation. When interviewing a suspect or a person of interest, the steps are:

1. Develop interview objectives (ie, what information needs to be known) prior to the start of the interview.

2. Establish the basis of the interview. This includes specifying whether the suspect is in custody and guilt seeking questions will be asked, thus necessitating the need for legal rights to be read or if the person of interest is free to leave the interview at any point.

3. Use a brief introduction and begin the building of a rapport with the interviewee based on the initial interview questions which involve topics such as place of employment, where they live, where they grew up, etc.

4. Use the opening statement to set the tone of the interview.

5. Ask what occurred and then listen carefully to the answer.

6. Ask them to start over and get further specific details (including what occurred before, during, and after the injury or event). In many cases, it is helpful for the investigator to pretend that they do not comprehend the person of interest's answers.

7. Obtain any other information required for the investigation. If the suspect denies the offense, the interviewer will need to challenge the denial. Many child abusers can be persuaded to tell the truth by an interviewer who is compassionate and able to clearly outline the detailed information that has been uncovered during this investigation. Challenging the suspect's denial must always be done in a respectful manner. Offenders will rarely (legally) confess to someone who is rude or disrespectful.

8. Bring the interview to conclusion without providing any specific information or disclosing the timeline of the investigation.

THE VICTIM INTERVIEW

Again, it is imperative that a child forensic interview specialist be utilized in cases where an interview of a child is to occur. In areas where this specialist is not available, it is important that agencies formulate a plan to employ one of these specialists or seek assistance for creating a position within the county. In cases where an investigator will be the sole interviewer, it is imperative for them to remember both the developmental level and the communicative abilities of the child, as well as the circumstances surrounding the interview. The investigator should be aware of young children's eating and sleeping schedules, avoiding interviews when they are hungry, tired, or otherwise uncomfortable.

To minimize the size differential, the interviewer should get on the same physical level as the child. The interviewer should also allow enough time to conduct the interview and consistently reassure the child that they are not in trouble or at fault. The interviewer should relate to the child at their developmental level and use language that is familiar to the child, keeping sentences simple. The child's words for their body parts should be used and the meaning of each term should be clarified. Pronouns should be used carefully to avoid confusion. The interviewer should remember to tell the child that it is okay to answer "I don't know" or "I don't understand" rather than to guess.

Furthermore, be aware of the child's nonverbal communication. The investigator should be conscious of his or her own body language as well, as it may affect the child's responsiveness during the interview. Do not use the investigator's or the child's body parts to evaluate the child's knowledge of anatomy.

CONDUCTING THE INTERVIEW

At the beginning of the interview, introductions should be made along with a simple explanation of the role of the interviewer. The interviewer must take time to establish rapport with the child. **Table 1-1** contains sample questions that can assist with establishing rapport.

Table 1-1. Sample Rapport-Building Questions

— What is your name? How old are you?

— Where do you live? Who lives with you? Who visits you?

— What are your mother's and father's names?

— What school do you go to? What grade are you in?

— What is your favorite subject? Least favorite?

— What is your teacher's name? Who was your teacher last year?

— What makes you happy? Sad? Mad? Scared?

— What do you like best about the people you live with? Least?

— What kind of things do you like to do alone?

These types of questions lead into more generalized questions that surround the case, potentially allowing the child to provide further information that was not previously learned, such as:

— Let's talk about your house, tell me who lives in your home?

— Tell me about your pets. What are their names? Describe them to me.

The investigator should ask as few direct questions as possible, but they should still attempt to obtain the what, who, how, where, and when of the allegation. **Table 1-2** shows examples of these types of questions.

Table 1-2. Questions That Can Be Asked of the Child Victim

TELL ME WHY YOU THINK YOU ARE HERE TODAY?

This question allows the child to describe the event in their own words.

If the child responds to this question by looking uncomfortable or does not want to talk about it, the interviewer should ask the child questions such as:

— You looked happy when we were talking about your favorite teacher, but now you look sad when I asked you why you are here today. Why is that?

— Did I say or do something to make you sad? Can you tell me about that?

Commenting on a child's obvious change in demeanor is not a leading question and will often allow the child to begin to acknowledge and disclose the abuse.

Help the child expand on the information by asking the following:

— What were you wearing? What was the [suspected perpetrator] wearing?

— What happened to your clothes? What happened to the [suspected perpetrator's] clothes?

— What did he or she say? What did you say to him or her?

— Who did you tell this to?

ARE YOU HURT OR SICK NOW?

Never delay emergency medical care. If the child indicates that they are hurt, ask where at and seek medical care, if necessary.

WHAT HAPPENED NEXT?

This question encourages more detail. When a child begins to disclose, you may prompt them with questions such as the following:

— What else do you remember? What else do I need to know?

— Could you tell me what you mean by [...]? I need to understand a little more about this.

— Were pictures taken? Of what? By whom? Where are the pictures?

— Were you asked not to tell anyone? Who asked you? What were you asked not to tell? Who were you not supposed to tell? This helps to determine the use of threats or bribes.

WHO DID THIS TO YOU?

If the information is not volunteered, it is important to ask the name of the abuser and their relationship to the victim.

— Were you touched by anyone? Who? Where?

— How do you know them?

— Has anyone else done this to you? Who? Where?

Continued

Table 1-2. Questions That Can Be Asked of the Child Victim *(continued)*

HOW DID THIS HAPPEN?

Asking this question will prompt an explanation for the event.

— What were you touched with? (An object may have been used.)

WHEN DID THIS HAPPEN?

Determining when the event happened may require association with other dates (eg, holidays, visits, day, and/or night.)

— Time of day? Month? Year? (With a younger child, you may need to link the event with any of the following: the clothes they were wearing, before or after a meal, during a television show, the weather, the beginning, middle, or end of the school year, birthdays, anniversaries, or holidays.)

— Has this happened before? When? Where? (If sexual abuse is alleged, look for grooming and events leading up to the act.)

Especially in intrafamilial cases, a child may have been abused on multiple occasions. These children will often use phrases such as "It usually happens…" or "Most of the time they do…". The interviewer should work with the child to identify specific incidences and then they should jointly label them (eg, "So, can we call that the 'time in the car' or 'the out in the barn time?'") Each incident should be reviewed with the child in order to obtain the details of what, who, when, and how.

Some child victims may acknowledge that an abusive incident occurred, but they are reluctant to provide details. The interviewer may be able overcome this resistance by asking the child what was happening leading up to the incident. This allows the child to begin their narrative account of less threatening aspects before progressing onto the more distressing details of the abusive incident.

WHO SAW THIS HAPPEN?

Asking this question corroborates witness information and addresses the possibility of multiple victims or suspected perpetrators.

— Was anyone else in the room when this happened? Who was there?

— Were you seen by anyone else? Who?

— Was there anyone else this happened to?

— If this happened to someone else, where were they touched? By whom?

— Was anyone else at home? Where were they?

CONCLUDING THE INTERVIEW

On completing the interview, ask the child if they have any questions, then answer the questions honestly. Comfort the child, but do not make promises that may not be kept. Ask the child what they expect to happen, then explain what is likely to happen. Inform the child of any further contacts or interviews. If additional interviews are needed, it is less traumatic for the child to answer questions from the same interviewer.

If the child has not disclosed abuse but there are indicators that abuse did take place, it may be necessary to refer the child to a qualified counselor. However, if prosecution is a possibility, counseling, therapy, or other abuse-related treatment (including hypnosis) could compromise the criminal case. Discuss such treatment with the prosecutor before arranging for these types of services.

INTERVIEWING WITNESSES

When interviewing a witness, first allow them to tell their version of events in a narrative style. To gather more detail and to jog the witness' memory, ask specific questions afterwards. Remember, the best interviewer is a great listener first.

When interviewing a witness, try to obtain a written statement, if possible, and be sure to ask the following questions:

— What is the correct spelling of the names, addresses, and phone numbers of the other persons who are mentioned in this event?

— Did the victim disclose the incident to you?

— Is there anything else you want to add that I have failed to ask you?

— Is there anything else that you want to discuss?

PRELIMINARY INVESTIGATIVE CHECKLIST

To facilitate a more timely and comprehensive assessment of the case, checklists are an excellent investigative aid (**Table 1-3**). They are a reminder to obtain specific information and provide a means for organizing and measuring the status of the investigation. Checklists can be tailored to meet most agency requirements. Remember, however, that the checklist is only a reminder and a guide; continue to make every effort to verify and expand on information as it becomes known. Clearly differentiate between investigative leads and verified facts.

Table 1-3. Preliminary Investigative Checklist

1. How was the allegation received?

   — By whom?

   — Has a child abuse and neglect hotline report been made?

   — Incident number?

   — Date?

   — Reporter?

   — County of incident?

2. Nature of the allegation(s)?

   — Who?

   — What?

   — When?

   — Where? (Exact location and venue)

   — How?

   — How many times?

3. Victim(s)—full pedigree?

   — Name?

   — Date of birth?

   — Race?

Continued

Table 1-3. Preliminary Investigative Checklist *(continued)*

    — Social Security number?

    — Child Protective Services (CPS) client number?

    — Home address, phone number, county?

    — Where the child(ren) lived at the time of this report (with parents, relatives, family, friends, foster care, kinship care, or describe some other arrangement)?

    — Is(are) the victim(s) at risk?

    — Protective custody taken?

    — Has(ve) the victim(s) been injured? If so, in need of medical treatment?

    — Sibling(s) in the home?

    — Sibling(s) at risk?

4. Parent(s)—full pedigree?

    — Father and/or mother's name?

    — Date of birth?

    — Race?

    — Social Security number?

    — CPS client number?

    — Home address, phone number, county?

    — Employer? Work phone number?

5. Name of guardian/caretaker(s)—full pedigree (if other than parent)?

    — Their date of birth?

    — Their race?

    — Their Social Security number?

    — Their CPS client number?

    — Their home address, phone number, county?

    — Their employer? Their work phone number?

    — Their relationship to the victim?

6. Medical treatment—was it needed?

    — Nature of the illness/injury?

    — When?

    — Where?

    — By whom?

    — Were photographs taken of injury? By whom?

7. If sexual abuse is alleged, has a sexual assault forensic examination been completed on the victim?

    — When?

    — Where?

    — By whom?

Continued

Table 1-3. Preliminary Investigative Checklist *(continued)*

— Findings?

— Colposcope or other image documentation used?

8. Has the victim been interviewed?

— By whom?

— When?

— Where?

— Recorded by audio or video?

9. Suspected perpetrator(s)—full pedigree?

— Name(s)?

— Date of birth?

— Race?

— Social Security number?

— CPS client number?

— Home address, phone number, county?

— Employer? Work phone number?

— Relationship to victim?

10. Records check completed?

— Local?

— State?

— FBI?

— Other applicable state(s)

— Social history?

— Child abuse and neglect hotline prior reports?

— Medical and health records?

11. Is there physical evidence?

— Description?

— Chain of custody?

— Present location?

12. Are there witnesses?

— Name(s)?

— Date of birth?

— Race?

— Social Security number?

— CPS client number?

— Home address, phone number, county?

— Employer? Work phone number?

— Relationship to victim?

Continued

Table 1-3. Preliminary Investigative Checklist *(continued)*

---

13. How documented statements been taken from witnesses and others?

    — From whom?

    — By whom?

14. CPS/juvenile court actions taken to date?

    — What?

    — When?

15. Criminal justice action taken to date?

    — Investigation in progress?

    — Charges pending?

    — Charges filed?

    — Arrest(s) made? If yes, is suspect still confined?

16. What agencies and investigators are involved in the investigation?

    — What are their responsibilities?

PREPARING FOR THE FUTURE

It is incumbent on investigators, especially ones employed by smaller agencies, to take the necessary steps to prepare themselves for these highly important and sensitive investigations. By properly planning with their police administration, as well as their local district attorney office, these investigators can be better prepared for maltreatment cases when they occur within their jurisdiction. Specialized interview training benefits the investigator assigned to the child victim crimes, but it also benefits other cases that small agency investigators handle as well. Being proactive and preplanning for these types of cases can mean the difference between a successful prosecution of a serial molester, for example, or releasing the suspect back into society.

SERIOUS CRIME/EVENT SCENE PROCEDURES

Officers responding to the scene of a reported incident must follow careful procedures to ensure the correct handling of the investigation. The guide in **Table 1-4** outlines the major steps to take at the scene of a reported crime, as well as offers specific information that is useful to law enforcement personnel.

Table 1-4. Guide for Law Enforcement Officers Responding to the Scene of a Reported Event

---

ASSIGNMENT OR NOTIFICATION

Officer safety is first and foremost when responding to any call for service. Record the time of assignment and arrival at the scene. Attempt to obtain all available information from the reporting person.

PRESERVE AND PROTECT LIFE

Determine if there are injuries or imminent dangers that require immediate attention. If injuries are present and there is any possibility of life, seek medical help immediately (make sure to obtain the names of medical personnel and other responders). Normally, the injured should not be moved before medical assistance arrives unless in immediate danger (eg, fire, water). Call for other assistance as necessary (eg, law enforcement, coroner/medical examiner, CPS, juvenile court officer, fire department, utility company).

Continued

Table 1-4. Guide for Law Enforcement Officers Responding to the Scene of a Reported Event *(continued)*

DETERMINE WHAT CRIME AND/OR EVENT HAS OCCURRED

Identify the victim(s) and witness(es); make a preliminary determination of what has occurred and what actions are required.

IF APPROPRIATE, IDENTIFY AND/OR ARREST SUSPECTED PERPETRATOR(S)

If a suspected perpetrator is identified but is not on the scene, obtain and broadcast a complete description including their name, alias(es), nickname (if available), race, sex, age and date of birth, address, physical description (eg, height, weight, hair length and color, eye color, complexion, scars, tattoos), clothing description, any other physical identifiers, vehicle, direction of flight, and a weapon description (if any). Broadcast the description and what the person is wanted for as soon as possible and update with new information as it becomes available.

If the suspected perpetrator is on the scene and is believed to be armed or is concealed and/or barricaded, request assistance and follow the investigative agency's policy.

If an immediate arrest is required, secure and search the suspected perpetrator as quickly as possible. For officer protection, search within the wingspan of the individual for anything that could cause harm. Any weapons, evidence, or contraband found during this search is able to be seized and is usually admissible as evidence.

NOTE: Safety and the protection and preservation of life are paramount. Do not take unnecessary risks.

ESTABLISH AND PROTECT THE CRIME/EVENT SCENE

Once identified, "freeze" the scene and everything in it. With the exception of assisting the injured, the crime/event scene should remain untouched, pending appropriate processing and photographing. If possible, secure and protect the perimeters with rope, tape, or other markers. Within manpower limitations, identify, separate, and isolate the witness(es) before interviewing.

NOTE: In the case of an obvious death (ie, no possibility of life), do not move the body or anything surrounding it before the coroner/medical examiner arrives. Photograph the body and scene before other processing procedures. While conveying a body to the morgue or other facility, depending on jurisdiction protocol, take necessary measures to protect the head and extremities from accidental damage (eg, paper bags on hands and feet). If the body is in rigor mortis, do not attempt to move or force extremities before moving it.

If the victim appears near death (and it does not interfere with medical assistance), attempt to obtain a dying declaration of what occurred.

NOTE: The sudden unexpected death of an infant (ie, a child 1 week to 1 year of age) is now referred to as sudden unexpected infant death (SUID). The cause of SUID remains unknown, but criteria for its diagnosis have been established by the National Institute of Child Health and Human Development. For the death of an infant to be diagnosed as SUID, an autopsy, clinical history review, and a thorough death scene investigation must be performed. In conducting these very sensitive and complex investigations, obtain all information available concerning social and medical history of the infant, as well as the death scene and circumstances surrounding the death.

PROCESS THE SCENE

Once the scene has been "frozen," develop investigative goals and objectives.

Determine the legal basis for any search and seizure, particularly beyond the immediate crime/event scene. Considering the investigative agency's policy and procedures, the prosecuting attorney should be consulted on specific legal questions, such as consent to search versus the need for a search warrant and other "search and seizure" issues. While it may be easier to seek the consent of a resident of the location, a search warrant provides more legal protection for the prosecution. The defense of a coerced search is often raised during suppression motions but can be avoided by taking the extra time to obtain a search warrant.

Establish a chain-of-custody log (ie, who found what and where) to be maintained by a single officer. Designate that person to receive and take charge of all physical evidence at the scene.

NOTE: Prior to seizing, all evidence should be photographed, with and without scale, sequentially numbered, and logged as found. Only designated persons should search the crime scene and handle evidence. All others, excluding emergency medical assistance personnel, should remain outside the protected area.

Continued

Table 1-4. Guide for Law Enforcement Officers Responding to the Scene of a Reported Event *(continued)*

Measurements should be taken and sketches should be made that relate directly to the photographs. All sketches should indicate which direction is north as well as be initialed and contain the investigators badge number.

A complete photographic sequence of the entire scene area, including a "landmark" photograph (eg, front of the house, vehicle license plate) should be taken. Complete and use photograph cards with a measuring scale when appropriate, as in close-ups or specific objects. Every phase of evidence handling should be documented.

Photographs and corresponding sketches should be taken from the general to the specific, from an overall room shot, to the bed, to a blood stain on the pillow. Again, all photographs should be taken with and without scale. Body pictures should be taken from at least 2 views and be full-length. Close-up photographs of wounds and abnormalities, when possible, should be visible in the full-length pictures.

Weapons and nontraditional surfaces (eg, paper, cardboard, leather, masonry) are best processed at the laboratory. Such evidence should be handled with care and is usually best transported in a paper or cardboard container. Evidence should always be processed using the department guidelines and current best practices, as technology evolves every day.

NOTE: All recovered and seized weapons should be considered loaded and dangerous until examined and deemed safe by a qualified person who is familiar with firearms.

All seized evidence should be properly marked, packaged, and placed in a secure evidence locker or conveyed to the appropriate laboratory for processing. A chain-of-custody log should track the handling of every piece of evidence. It is essential that evidence be handled and packaged in containers appropriate for the material. Some evidence should be sealed and frozen, while others require air drying or special containers. Consult a crime laboratory or crime scene processing specialist for specific evidence handling instructions.

INTERVIEW/INTERROGATION PROCESS

The suspected perpetrator(s) and witnesses should be separated and interviewed individually.

The suspected perpetrator(s) should be interrogated relative to their part in the crime/event. Improbabilities and inconsistencies should be noted and used to enhance the questioning process. Contradicting statements can be an important part of the case. It is important for the interviewer to lock-in the suspect's alibi or explanation so that it can be proven or disproven.

NOTE: Follow the investigative agency's policy and procedures for advising suspected perpetrators of their Miranda rights and obtaining verbal and written waiver of those rights.

SUMMARY

As outlined in this chapter, the investigation of child maltreatment is one of the more difficult assignments that a police officer can face during their career. In a vast majority of these maltreatment cases, the interviews that are conducted serve as the linchpin that brings the case to the point of charges. It is imperative that the investigator of a child maltreatment case know proper interview techniques as well as their limitations when it comes to the delicate nature of interviewing children. Lastly, interviewers/investigators should always conduct themselves with the utmost accountability, integrity, and professionalism in order to bring justice to the victims of these heinous crimes.

ADDITIONAL RESOURCES

1. Monteleone JA. *Recognition of Child Abuse for the Mandated Reporter*. 4th ed. STM Learning, Inc; 2015.

2. Pence D, Wilson C. *Team Investigation of Child Sexual Abuse*. Sage Publications; 1994.

3. Walker AG. *Handbook of Questioning Children: A Linguistic Perspective*. 3rd ed. ABA on Children and the Law; 2017.

The Review Process and Child Fatality Review Teams

Vincent Palusci, MD, MS, FAAP

Objectives

After reviewing this chapter, the reader will be able to:

1. *Understand the implications of child fatality in cases of maltreatment.*

2. *Describe the current epidemiology, risk factors, and presentation of fatal child maltreatment.*

3. *Describe fatal child abuse task force recommendations and understand the need for accurate, systematic review of child deaths.*

4. *List the purposes and aims of child fatality review in the United States.*

5. *Discuss the benefits of child fatality review programs.*

6. *Discuss the important roles of pediatricians and other professionals in the child death review process.*

The Implications of Fatality After Child Maltreatment

The death of a child is a sentinel event in a community, prompting the need to understand the cause of the child's death and how to then prevent additional child deaths. When a child's death is caused by abuse or neglect, it reflects modifiable psychosocial factors rather than biologic causes.[1] In addition a substantial number of children who died as a result of maltreatment were previously reported to Child Protective Services (CPS), thus demonstrating that the child's death was preventable.[2] Preventable deaths from child neglect and maltreatment give communities the opportunity to create strategies that identify families at risk, provide services that can reduce said risk, and then intervene to best help the families and surviving children.

Child fatality review (CFR) teams, sometimes called child death review teams, have been developed across the United States in order to better assist with the proper identification of the causes of child deaths and to design community and organizational interventions aimed at preventing future child deaths. This chapter reviews the current epidemiology, risk factors, and presentation of fatal child maltreatment, discusses how systematic reviews of child deaths can help prevent future deaths, and demonstrates the importance of pediatricians and other professionals in assisting the community CFR process.

EPIDEMIOLOGY, RISK FACTORS, AND PRESENTATION OF FATAL CHILD ABUSE

It has been suggested by professionals of various sectors (eg, law, medicine, social work, etc.) that society needs to dramatically redesign its approach to helping families and children; the goal is to place a stronger focus on prevention, thus eliminating child abuse and neglect fatalities.[3] Despite more than 25 years of administrative data, CFR teams, and a national CFR case collection system, there is still only limited research on child fatality prevention, and it is difficult to measure whether prevention efforts have actually resulted in a reduction of child maltreatment fatalities. Without an accurate national count of child maltreatment fatalities, it is impossible to truly know if sufficient improvements have been made.[3,4] In addition, low incidence rates, a myriad of potential causes (eg, positional asphyxia deaths misidentified as sudden infant death syndrome [SIDS], neglect labelled as an accident, etc.), and the inability to predict accurate child maltreatment fatalities in infants and young children, have made prevention difficult.[4]

An estimated 1770 children died as a result of maltreatment in the United States in 2018, a rate of 2.4 per every 100 000 children.[2] This number has increased in the last 20 years, from 2000 to 2020 (**Figure 2-1**). In more than 70% of the fatal cases, children were under the age of 3 years, and most of those deaths occurred as a result of neglect alone (73% in 2018) or in combination with abuse. This number is thought to be an undercount, however, with the actual amount being 2 or 3 times larger than that reported in official statistics.[2,3] Child maltreatment fatality has historically been under ascertained in the United States, leading to inadequate response to and prevention of future deaths.[3]

Figure 2-1. United States child abuse deaths recorded in the National Child Abuse and Neglect Data System. (Figure adapted from US Department of Health & Human Services, Administration for Children & Families, Children's Bureau, National Child Abuse and Neglect Data System website.)

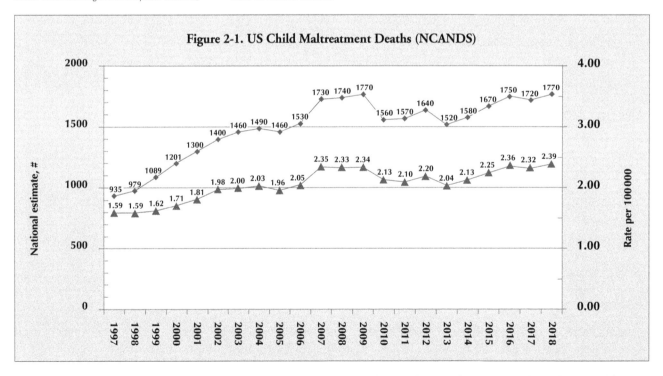

There are a number of confirmed factors that increase the risk for child abuse fatality, but these factors vary depending on the population studied (eg, emergency departments, inpatients, medical examiner offices). Certain child, family, and community factors can play into risk levels as well.[5-9] Infants and toddlers have the highest risk for an abuse or neglect fatality compared to other age groups and require special attention. Schnitzer and Ewigman[5] found that children under

5 years of age who lived in households with male adults who were not biologically related to them were 50 times more likely to die from inflicted injury compared to children residing in households with 2 biological parents. Substance abuse, as well as access to and use of drugs and alcohol, are also risk factors.[6] Douglas and Mohn[10] found that children who were fatally maltreated lived in families that experienced more financial and housing instability compared to non-fatally maltreated children and used or received fewer social services.

Although several causes of death require medical inspection to identify (eg, abusive head trauma, blunt trauma, asphyxiation, poisoning, neglect), child maltreatment fatalities are not solely a medical problem, but are also connected to family problems, social conditions, and other community violence issues.[11] In 2016, 29.7% of children who died had at least 1 prior CPS contact in the 3 years preceding their death. Similarly, in 2018, 20.3% of child fatality cases had received family preservation services within 5 years preceding the child's death.[2] A prior call to a child protection hotline, regardless of its disposition, is the best predictor of a later child maltreatment or neglect fatality.[6] CPS plays an important part in protecting children, but it is not clear how or whether CPS's prevention efforts should target children with specific risk factors when a case involving their family has previously been reported.[12] The uncertainty associated with CPS demonstrates the need for a policy discussion, and perhaps even a policy change, regarding CPS's role, how it responds to calls, and whether an initial decision to "screen out" certain calls leaves children, who may be at a high risk for later death, unseen.[3]

Abusive families differ statistically from non-abusive families in many regards, but it is difficult to identify families with risk for fatality since severely abusive and mildly abusive families share the same demographic features and are largely indistinguishable. In addition, child abuse fatalities have many of the same risk factors as found among children with an undetermined manner of death.[13] Thus, all child fatalities must be thoroughly reviewed in order to gain a comprehensive understanding of child maltreatment-related deaths.

Currently, there are limited criteria available that help experts discern whether risk factors indicate mild or severe cases of child maltreatment. The most common risk factors seem to relate to the caregivers' previous use of aggression and physical violence toward the child, especially if they have a record of assault and/or exhibited aggressive behaviors during their childhood. Based on this and the risk factors mentioned above, prevention efforts should be targeted toward newborns and very young children (eg, newborns with perinatal risk factors, infants who are not receiving medical care, infants who are not brought for follow-up medical treatments, families with live-in boyfriends, and families with criminal records).[1-7]

THE RECOMMENDATIONS OF CHILD FATALITY TASK FORCES

The US Commission to Eliminate Child Abuse and Neglect Fatalities (CECANF) was created in response to a Government Accountability Office report[14] that raised issues with the country's national identification procedures as well as its response to child abuse and neglect deaths. CECANF[3] found that the current array of services and support systems in the United States did not adequately ensure accurate counting, or safety, for children at increased risk for fatality (**Table 2-1**). An example of the inaccurate, and oftentimes blatant, undercount of child maltreatment is found in a study conducted by the Centers for Disease Control and Prevention (CDC) of the reporting systems in 3 states: California, Michigan, and Rhode Island. The study concluded that there was no consistent system for counting child deaths and that ultimately "official" death counts were underreported, hindering the much-needed accurate information for creating prevention plans.[15] This particular CDC study also concluded that CFR may be the most promising approach for ensuring the most accurate case ascertainments.

Table 2-1. US National Commission, 2016

FINDINGS & RECOMMENDATIONS	— Child abuse deaths are undercounted
	— Need to identify children and families most at risk
	— Need to know injuries associated with fatal abuse
	— Agencies need to be accountable
	— Federal government should provide leadership and funding
	— Conduct fatality reviews using similar processes across jurisdictions

Table adapted from the Findings and Recommendations of the US Commission on the Elimination of Child Abuse and Neglect Fatalities.[3]

DEVELOPMENT OF CHILD FATALITY REVIEW IN THE UNITED STATES

CFR is a multidisciplinary examination of individual child deaths that is aimed at gaining a better understanding of the risk factors and circumstances surrounding the death of a child. CFR teams are made up of community members of various disciplines and backgrounds (eg, race, gender, socioeconomic status, geography, literacy, sexual orientation, and gender identity) who convene in an effort to recommend prevention efforts. Death certificates and vital records provide basic information on how children die, but they lack details on why or what risk factors existed within the child, family, community, and/or environment that may have resulted in a child's death. The role of CFR teams is not to place blame on individuals or agencies but to identify and address system gaps.[16-18]

While the exact origin of CFR is difficult to trace, it is believed that the first review teams originated in the late 1970s. During the 1980s, CFR teams began expanding, in large part, due to grassroots efforts. In the 1990s and early 2000s, CFR continued to grow within the United States, and several pieces of federal legislation were passed to support it. Most notably, the Child Abuse Prevention and Treatment Act (CAPTA) required states to include fatality data in their program plans. CAPTA now not only requires states to review child fatalities, but it requires that states have a comprehensive plan for engaging a broad group of stakeholders, including law enforcement, private agencies, and public health officials. CAPTA also requires that data be made available to the public.[19] Given the similarities between CAPTA reviews and CFR teams, many states worked to build a collaboration between the 2 systems, with some states even using CFR teams to fulfill their CAPTA requirements.[20]

In 1993, a landmark study in the journal *Pediatrics* demonstrated the underreporting of child abuse deaths based on CFR conducted in Missouri.[21] The first national convention on CFR teams took place in 1994, and representatives from 43 states attended. By the end of 1995, the US Advisory Board on Child Abuse and Neglect reported that 45 states were consistently reviewing child deaths.[1] In 2002, the US Health Resources and Services Administration funded the first national resource center for CFR. CFR programs now exist in all 50 states, the District of Columbia, and on many tribal reservations.[22]

CFR programs operate in 3 ways, following 3 different models.[22] The first is a state level program where case review, data collection, and written recommendations are done statewide. This process is common in geographically small states or those with low population density, which therefore often have fewer deaths. Secondly, some CFR programs have local teams, typically county-based, that review deaths and collect data. The third structure is a hybrid of the other 2, whereby a state team writes recommendations based on data gathered from reviews conducted by local teams. The hybrid state/local structure is the most common within the United States and is effective because it maximizes local access to records and first responders while leveraging state relationships to make policy changes, which allows the team to better understand the circumstances beyond just case notes and official reports.

The membership of CFR teams varies depending on state or local laws, jurisdictional needs, and the type of death under review.[16] At a minimum, it is recommended that CFR teams be composed of a member of law enforcement, a death certifier (medical examiner/coroner), a public health official, a pediatrician, a child welfare official, and a prosecuting attorney. Many teams also include members from emergency medical services, schools, hospitals, community mental health centers, fire departments, and community outreach programs such as Healthy Start or Zero to Three. Team members come to each meeting with case information regarding specific children and share what is known with the team, and then teams are tasked with catalyzing prevention based on the review meeting and data collected.

By sharing the collected data in local reviews with state fatality review teams, data trends are identified and action can be taken across jurisdictions. Additionally, state fatality review teams can recommend changes and shifts in agency policy and practices. These reviews must happen at the state level so as to identify and correct systemic barriers, therefore protecting children and ensuring a coordinated approach to the problem. The review committee must have access to all relevant records, including social services reports, court documents, police records, autopsy records, mental health records, and hospital or medical-related data.[16]

Over time, the National Center for Fatality Review and Prevention[22] has identified that the most successful states using CFR have legislation that:

— Allows the state access to records without parental consent

— Allows subpoena for records when needed (This is particularly important for school and mental health records.)

— Gives broad guidance for the review of cases without being so specific that any deviation requires legislative change (An example of this is COVID. Some states have such limiting legislation that they cannot review deaths due to COVID since they are considered natural.)

— Requires membership from core agencies but still gives the team enough flexibility to add members when needed

— Identifies leadership for the team

— Provides funding

— Requires reports from CFR findings and a response from elected officials

THE IMPORTANT ROLE OF PEDIATRICIANS

By compiling records from many disciplines, CFR teams can examine a child's death with a new perspective. Often, individual agencies are unaware of how other agencies respond to a child death; therefore, it is important to ensure that the team reflects the community it serves and includes key professionals such as pediatric medical providers.[23]

Pediatricians understand the complete and complex needs of young children and their families and can help design and implement the strategies that are needed in the context of their communities. Pediatricians and other pediatric medical providers have a unique understanding of child development and the importance of well-child care, and they provide anticipatory guidance for families on a number of child safety issues, making them invaluable members of the CFR team. Professional organizations such as the American Academy of Pediatrics and the American Professional Society on the Abuse of Children have developed guidelines and training for pediatricians and other professionals to understand CFR, integreate prevention into practice, and help families and communities respond to the death of a child.[25-27]

INTERVENTIONS DEVELOPED BY CHILD FATALITY REVIEW PROGRAMS

There are a number of potentially beneficial interventions that have been developed by CFR teams. Those are[24]:

— The encouragement of state "safe haven" laws that allow parents to drop off newborns and young infants at hospitals, police stations, and firehouses in an effort to decrease newborn deaths

— The promotion of a back sleep position for healthy infants in an effort to decrease rates of SIDS

— The education of parents and caregivers on safe sleeping arrangements and dangerous bedding products

— The verification of working smoke detectors in the home and establishment of fire escape routes

— The discussion of appropriate disciplinary methods

— The discussion of age-appropriate behaviors for children and unrealistic expectations of parents

— The discussion of the risks associated with shaking an infant

— The discussion of age-appropriate supervision

SUMMARY

Child maltreatment fatality is a sentinel event that has been undercounted in the United States, leading to inadequate community responses and increasing child deaths. CFR teams have been developed to assist in improving child maltreatment identification, rooting out the causes of said maltreatment, and designing community and organizational interventions that can prevent future child deaths. This chapter has explored the current epidemiology, risk factors, and presentation of fatal child maltreatment, the recommendations of task forces on fatal child maltreatment, and the development of CFR in the United States. There are several important benefits of CFR programs, and pediatricians and other community professionals play a paramount role in this process.

REFERENCES

1. US Advisory Board on Child Abuse and Neglect. A nation's shame: fatal child abuse and neglect in the United States. Child Welfare Information Gateway. April 1995. https://library.childwelfare.gov/cwig/ws/library/docs/gateway/Blob/27598.pdf;jsessionid=7EE7AE3D4E24D0C39AE7EFB241D20480?r=1&rpp=25&upp=0&w=NATIVE%28%27AUTHORS+ph+like+%27%27Advisory+Board%27%27%27%29&m=22&order=native-%28%27year%2Fdescend%27%29

2. US Department of Health and Human Services, Children's Bureau. Child maltreatment 2018. Administration for Children and Families. January 15, 2020. Updated June 12, 2020. https://www.acf.hhs.gov/cb/research-data-technology/statistics-research/child-maltreatment

3. Commission to Eliminate Child Abuse and Neglect Fatalities. Within our reach: a national strategy to eliminate child abuse and neglect fatalities. Administration for Children and Families. 2016. https://www.acf.hhs.gov/sites/default/files/documents/cb/cecanf_final_report.pdf

4. Barth RP, Putnam-Hornstein E, Shaw TV, Dickinson NS. Safe children: reducing severe and fatal maltreatment. American Academy of Social Work and Social Welfare. 2016. Accessed 2021. https://grandchallengesforsocialwork.org/wp-content/uploads/2015/12/WP17-with-cover.pdf

5. Schnitzer PG, Ewigman BG. Child deaths resulting from inflicted injuries: household risk factors and perpetrator characteristics. *Pediatrics*. 2005;116:687-693.

6. Putnam-Hornstein E. Report of maltreatment as a risk factor for injury death: a prospective birth cohort study. *Child Maltreat*. 2011;16:163-174.

7. Farrell CA, Fleegler EW, Monuteaux MC, Wilson CR, Christian CW, Lee LK. Community poverty and child abuse fatalities in the United States. *Pediatrics*. 2017;139(5):20161616. doi:10.1542/peds.2016-1616

8. Palusci VJ, Kay AJ, Batra E, et al. Identifying child abuse fatalities during infancy. *Pediatrics*. 2019;144(3):20192076. doi:10.1542/peds.2019-2076

9. Kennedy JM, Lazoritz S, Palusci VJ. Risk factors for child maltreatment fatalities in a national pediatric inpatient database. *Hosp Pediatr*. 2020;10(3):230-237. doi:10.1542/hpeds.2019-0229

10. Douglas EM, Mohn BL. Fatal and non-fatal child maltreatment in the US: an analysis of child, caregiver, and service utilization with the national child abuse and neglect data set. *Child Abuse Negl*. 2014;38:42-51.

11. Palusci VJ, Covington TM. Child maltreatment deaths in the US national child fatality review case reporting system. *Child Abuse Negl*. 2014;38(1):25-36.

12. Palusci VJ, Wirtz SJ, Covington TM. Using capture–recapture methods to better ascertain the incidence of fatal child maltreatment. *Child Abuse Negl*. 2010;34:396-402.

13. Bechtel K, Derbyshire M, Gaither JR, Leventhal JM. Characteristics that distinguish abusive from nonabusive causes of sudden unexpected infant deaths. *Pediatr Emerg Care*. 2019. doi:10.1097/PEC.0000000000001787

14. United States Government Accountability Office. Child maltreatment: strengthening national data on child fatalities could aid in prevention. US Government Accountability Office. July 2011. Accessed 2020. https://www.gao.gov/new.items/d11599.pdf

15. Schnitzer PG, Covington TM, Wirtz SJ, Verhoek-Oftedahl M, Palusci VJ. Public health surveillance of fatal child maltreatment: analysis of 3 state programs. *Am J Public Health*. 2008;98:296-303.

16. National Center for Fatality Review and Prevention; Child Death Review Leaders and Advocates throughout the US. A program manual for child death review: strategies to better understand why children die & taking action to prevent child deaths. National Center for Fatality Review and Prevention. September 2005. Accessed 2021. https://www.ncfrp.org/wp-content/uploads/NCRPCD-Docs/ProgramManual.pdf

17. Ornstein A, Bowes M, Shouldice M, Yanchar NL; Canadian Paediatric Society, Injury Prevention Committee and Child and Youth Maltreatment Section. The importance of child and youth death review. *Paediatr Child Health.* 2013;18(8):425-432.

18. Hochstadt NJ. Child fatality review teams: a vital component of child protection. *Child Welfare.* 2006;85(4):653-670.

19. Child abuse and neglect fatalities. National Conference of State Legislatures. April 13, 2016. Accessed 2020. https://www.ncsl.org/research/human-services/child-fatality-legislation.aspx

20. Palusci VJ, Yager S, Covington TM. Effects of a citizens review panel in preventing child maltreatment fatalities. *Child Abuse Negl.* 2010;34:324-331.

21. Ewigman B, Kivlahan C, Garland L. The Missouri child fatality study: underreporting of maltreatment fatalities among children younger than five years of age, 1983 through 1986. *Pediatrics.* 1993;91(2):330-337.

22. Keeping kids alive: child death review in the United States, 2018. National Center for Fatality Review and Prevention. June 2020. https://www.ncfrp.org/wp-content/uploads/Status_CDR_in_US_2018.pdf

23. Berger RP, Sanders D, Rubin D; Commission to Eliminate Abuse and Neglect Fatalities. Pediatricians' role in preventing child maltreatment fatalities: a call to action. *Pediatrics.* 2015;136(5):825-827. doi:10.1542/peds.2015-1776

24. Douglas EM, Ahola SB, Proulx ML. An exploratory analysis of the notable activities of US child death review teams. *Death Stud.* 2018;42(4):239-246.

25. Committee on Child Abuse and Neglect; Committee on Injury, Violence, and Poison Prevention; Council on Community Pediatrics. American academy of pediatrics, policy statement-child fatality review. *Pediatrics.* 2010;126(3):592-596. doi:10.1542/peds.2010-2006

26. Palusci VJ, Haney ML. Strategies to prevent child maltreatment and integration into practice. *APSAC Advisor.* 2010;22(1):8-17.

27. Palusci VJ, Devinsky O, Drake SA, et al. Family needs and follow-up care after the sudden, unexpected death of a child. In: Bundock EA, Corey TS, eds. *Unexplained Pediatric Deaths: Investigation, Certification and Family Needs.* Academic Forensic Pathology International; 2020:177-202.

The Role of the Medical Examiner in Child Fatality Investigations

Rachel Thomas, PhD, APRN-BC
Randell Alexander, MD, PhD

Objectives

After reviewing this chapter, the reader will be able to:

1. *Explain the role and professional responsibilities of the medical examiner (ME) in deaths where child abuse or neglect is suspected.*

2. *Understand the terminology commonly used by MEs.*

3. *Understand the differential diagnoses for early childhood fatalities.*

4. *List the indicators of a possible death due to sudden infant death syndrome (SIDS).*

5. *Discuss the elements of a trauma-informed approach to child death investigations, as well as the role of child death review (CDR) teams.*

Medical Examiners and Coroners

Coroners

While many references use the terms "medical examiner" and "coroner" interchangeably, such as medical examiner/coroner or ME/C offices, there are distinct differences between the 2 roles. Typically, MEs work in urban environments with larger populations. In rural areas, the coroner, who is often an elected official and not a physician, will have the responsibility of overseeing the details related to the death, including the maintenance of the body and the preservation of any forensic evidence. Coroners typically hold roles such as funeral home directors or law enforcement personnel.

Medical Examiners

MEs are board-certified physicians with in-depth training in anatomy, physiology, medicine, and forensic pathology. To be certified as an ME, one must complete medical school, residency, and 1 or more fellowships that are post-residency training. The ME conducts detailed autopsies and scene investigations as part of an overall death investigation to determine the cause and manner of death in unexplained circumstances, especially among those who "die outside of the health care system or die precipitously without a confirmed diagnosis."[1]

The importance of the ME's involvement in death investigations is twofold. Not only do they help elucidate causes of unexplained deaths, but their involvement may also contribute to a better understanding of societal, health, and public safety issues (eg, emerging infectious diseases, bioterrorism, teen suicides, the opioid crisis and drug overdoses, poisonings, motor vehicles accidents, etc.).[1]

According to a 2019 American Academy of Pediatrics Task Force,[2] having a skilled ME is crucial to avoid mislabeling the death or erroneously missing a case of child maltreatment. This task force states, "when a healthy infant dies suddenly and unexpectedly, it is critical to correctly determine if the death was caused by child abuse or neglect...[as] missing a child abuse death can place other children at risk, and inappropriately [labeling a death] can result in inappropriate criminal and protective services investigations."

MEs are involved in the investigations of roughly 20% of all reported deaths in the United States,[1] and they provide expertise in differentiating natural causes of death from other, often elusive, causes. In young infants and children, the ME's evaluations include diagnosing for a wide variety of differential causes of death such as congenital anomalies (eg, undetected heart defects), systemic infections (eg, meningitis), and sleep-related causes (eg, positional asphyxia or sudden unexpected infant death [SUID]). Child neglect and intentional abuse are other causes of early, unexplained childhood fatalities in previously well children.

Many ME offices have advanced diagnostic equipment in order to assist in the compilation of a thorough differential diagnosis pertaining to the cause of death. While performing an autopsy, the ME conducts careful macroscopic and microscopic assessments of the body with special attention to the cranium, cranial contents, and vital organs. They also collect tissue samples for further histological analysis and may send out specimens (eg, eyes) to specialists such as ophthalmologists and/or other forensic experts.

Ultimately, the training between coroners and MEs is quite different. Research has shown that in places with more coroners and less MEs, the causes of deaths tend to be unreported, under-recognized, or poorly understood.[3] While some smaller, rural communities may still use elected coroners as opposed to MEs, ME involvement has become increasingly important as medicine and medicolegal death investigations evolve. At present, nearly half of the United States' population is served by a coroner and half by a ME.[4]

THE MEDICAL EXAMINER AND CHILD DEATH INVESTIGATIONS

The ME's role in the investigation of any child's death that involved suspected maltreatment consists of:

— Identifying the presence and nature of injuries and/or underlying illnesses/ pathology

— Documenting pertinent findings (eg, positive and negative tests)

— Properly collecting and preserving evidence

— Evaluating any modifying or contributing factors (injuries and disease)

— Establishing time of injury/injuries and death

— Presenting findings in appropriate legal forums

In general, any sudden and unexpected death, or one wherein an injury or "non-natural" condition is suspected to have caused or contributed to the death, should be reported to the medicolegal authority in whose jurisdiction it falls. By their very nature, all deaths suspected to involve abuse or neglect must be brought to the attention of the applicable medicolegal authority. State laws often require sudden unexpected deaths in children under 5 years of age to be investigated and the child autopsied.

Two important terms for MEs to know and understand are **cause of death** and **manner of death**. These are defined as:

— **Cause of death:** The disease or injury, or a combination of the 2, that initiates the continuous series of events, however brief or prolonged, that culminates in death. The cause of death can be immediate or remote/underlying, and this determination is made after a thorough autopsy and medical history examination. There may be multiple causes of death or even secondary causes in some instances.

— **Manner of death:** The fashion in which the cause of death arises, taking into consideration the circumstances in which the individual died. The manner of death is traditionally classified as natural, homicide, accident, suicide, or undetermined.

The ME pays special attention to the timing of the death. This is typically determined from certain details about the body, such as temperature, changes in color, and/or rigor. Findings of rigor mortis (ie, pallor and stiffness), algor mortis (ie, low temperature), and lividity (ie, pooling of blood in gravity-dependent areas) help the ME determine when the individual died, and often, the position in which they died. Furthermore, both the gross and microscopic details are evaluated to help distinguish acute and older injuries.

INVESTIGATION

During the fatality investigation, the ME and their staff pay careful attention to the circumstances of the death and gather important details about the person who died. These can include anything that may have directly or indirectly contributed to the death, such as prescription medications or other drugs, alcohol, weapons, or ligatures.[5]

Many important facts pertaining to whether the manner of death was a homicide, suicide, natural death, or accident can be deduced from a careful examination of the scene and the individual's body. The ME or law enforcement officials will secure the scene so that forensic data can be preserved and samples can be collected from body fluids, splash patterns, residue, and other trace evidence.

In addition, video reenactments during the investigation period may help the ME determine if the history of trauma is consistent with the injuries or if they are a result of physical maltreatment. Video demonstrations are particularly helpful in cases of SUID because they detail the sleep position and circumstances of the sleeping environment.

TRAUMA-INFORMED APPROACH

The death of an infant or child may cause emotional distress for caregivers, medical personnel, and investigators in the direct aftermath of trauma and perhaps for a long time thereafter. Trauma-informed care principles should be implemented in all interactions with family members, whether the surviving relatives are perceived as "suspicious" or not. Properly navigating this tense environment is necessary not only for the ME and their staff, but also for law enforcement and Child Protective Services (CPS) workers who often arrive at the scene/decedent's home shortly after emergency medical services.

The ME must consider the emotional toll that early childhood deaths have on surviving relatives who are searching for causality and should therefore approach the investigation and all interactions with the surviving family members in a nonjudgmental manner. MEs should do their best to keep the death investigation free of bias.

DIFFERENTIAL DIAGNOSIS IN EARLY CHILDHOOD FATALITIES

For childhood fatalities, there are numerous potential causes of death. Fortunately, due to advances in the modern health care system, many former causes of early death are now able to be detected and treated as early as in utero, during the prenatal period, or by neonatologists shortly after the infant is delivered.

Widespread metabolic screening, such as a phenylketonuria analysis, syphilis screening, and HIV testing, are examples of early interventions that have decreased premature childhood deaths. Early and more frequent ultrasounds may also detect many potentially life-threatening congenital anomalies (eg, defects of the heart and spine). The prevalence of highly skilled geneticists, neonatologists, and more widespread availability of neonatal intensive care units have all resulted in sharp decreases in neonatal and infant deaths. In addition, genetic testing for potential diseases and disorders, including cystic fibrosis, Down syndrome, and other autosomal/inherited health issues, is now widely available in the United States.

Due to this widespread early disease detection through prenatal testing, antenatal testing, and postpartum intervention, the risk of early childhood deaths has dropped substantially over the decades. Thus, early childhood deaths often warrant intervention by police and CPS.

ASSESSMENT OF SLEEP-RELATED DEATHS IN INFANCY

To ensure that child maltreatment or other causes of death are not missed, most states require an autopsy of any infant who has died from SIDS. SIDS is a subset of SUID, but it should be noted that the term SUID is favored by the Centers for Disease Control and Prevention and used more often to label such deaths.[6] By definition, SIDS occurs in an infant under 12 months of age who has:

— A normal autopsy

— An unrevealing medical history

— An unrevealing scene investigation[7]

SIDS has been widely associated with the prone sleeping position and the sharing of a bed between infants and adult caregivers. Through a better understanding of sleep-related deaths and prevention efforts that include parental education on the use of firm sleep surfaces, supine sleeping positions, and avoidance of bed-sharing, these types of deaths have successfully been reduced.

FINDINGS THAT ARE SUSPICIOUS FOR CHILD MALTREATMENT

The ME is responsible for assessing the deceased infant or child for signs of pneumonia, aspiration, heart defects, internal bleeding, and/or signs of trauma. Assessment for both internal and external trauma is particularly important when previously healthy infants and young children die unexpectedly. Neglect, with or without physical abuse, is the most common cause of maltreatment-related fatalities in childhood.[2]

Oftentimes, external signs of physical abuse are apparent to investigators who arrive early to the scene. These signs include: contusions, hematomas, human bites, pinch marks, ligature injuries, petechiae, signs of blunt force trauma, and/or genital area trauma. Internal injuries are common among children who suffer fatal physical abuse. In some cases, internal trauma may have been the cause of death, especially if there were traumatic injuries to the head and/or visceral organs.

Head trauma and battering are the leading causes of death in very young victims of fatal child physical abuse. One longitudinal study[8] of 45 child abuse deaths over

6 years reported that victims were more likely to be male and have a median age of 1 year. Nearly half of the children died from internal head trauma. Researchers also found that "battered baby syndrome" accounted for approximately 15% of the deaths.

The same study[8] found that in 80% of those cases, relatives were involved as alleged perpetrators, and the child's father specifically was most often implicated (36.1%). Furthermore, 88.9% of fatal child maltreatment cases occurred within the family's residence. Child abuse professionals have identified several common themes among early childhood maltreatment fatalities. These are:

— A predominance of male victims

— A predominance of young victims, typically under the age of 5 years

— Deaths are usually caused by male household members, such as the mother's significant other or the child's biological father

— A prevalence of social risk factors in the home such as family violence or repeated involvement with CPS and/or law enforcement

— Deaths are most often caused by blunt trauma to internal organs, especially head injuries and thoracoabdominal trauma

Bruises (ie, contusions) are often found in living child maltreatment victims as well as normal, active children who are appropriately nurtured. Bruises on the knees, elbows, or other bony prominences are locations typically consistent with normal childhood activities. Excessive bruising distributed throughout the body, however, is very unusual and suspicious for maltreatment, especially if an underlying bleeding disorder, such as hemophilia, has been excluded by serum analysis and a careful medical history. Bruises in young, non-mobile infants are extremely uncommon and should raise suspicions of maltreatment.[9]

The TEN4- FACESp clinical decision rule is an acronym used to differentiate accidental bruising from physical abuse (**Table 3-1**). Although some of these physical examination findings are subtle, an astute ME may be alerted to look for other specific signs of child abuse and subsequently classification of the death as a homicide.[10,11]

Table 3-1. Explanation of the TEN4- FACESp Mnemonic Device

— Any bruising of the **T**orso, **E**ars or **N**eck in Children age **4 months or under**

— Bruising anywhere on the body of an infant under the age of 1 year—and especially those **under 4 months**—who is not yet mobile (eg, crawling, pulling to a standing position, or cruising)

— **F**renulum injuries or lacerations to the upper or lower lingual frenulum or the sublingual frenulum

— **A**ngle of the jaw

— **C**heek contusions

— **E**yelid, external eye, or orbital area contusions

— **S**cleral hemorrhages affecting the white of the eye(s)

— **p**atterned bruising that resembles an object, such as a blunt force instrument, belt, cord, paddle, shoe, hairbrush, or other available household object that could be used as a weapon

---

Other pertinent findings that are indicative of possible maltreatment as a contributing or main cause of death include:

— Acute burns and burn scars

— Poisoning and toxin ingestion/exposure

— Extreme neglect, failure to thrive, and severe malnutrition (eg, cachexia)

Signs of child sexual trauma that may be present in unexplained deaths among females include:

— Genital area bruises, lacerations, or scars, especially involving recessed anatomical areas such as the posterior fourchette, fossa navicularis, or hymen

— Acute lacerations of the posterior rim of the hymen, particularly if they are below the 3 o'clock and 9 o'clock positions

— Missing portions of hymen below the 3 o'clock and 9 o'clock positions

— Anal area bruises and/or lacerations

— Sexually transmitted infections (STIs)

— Pregnancy

— Human bite marks in intimate areas of the body (eg, inner thighs, neck, breasts)

Signs of child sexual trauma that may present in unexplained deaths among males include:

— Anal area bruises and/or lacerations

— STIs

— Injuries of the genitals, including bruises and lacerations of the penis, scrotum, or testicles

— Human bite marks in intimate areas of the body (eg, inner thighs)[12]

CHILD DEATH REVIEW TEAMS

In the United States, CDR teams are composed of a multidisciplinary representation of professionals within the investigative field. CDR teams are typically tasked with reviewing the deaths that have been reported to law enforcement agencies or CPS. In these cases, the ME's role is to present and explain their autopsy findings to the rest of the team.

The causes of deaths reviewed by CDR teams are often from preventable events, such as sleep-related deaths, drownings, motor vehicle crashes, and/or poisoning/ingestions. However, some of the investigated child deaths are from intentional causes (eg, physical abuse, homicide), and some are from neglect (eg, unsafe sleeping conditions/ positions, drowning). Findings from the CDR team help to better elucidate common causes of and contributions to child deaths that, in turn, inform prevention efforts. Many state CDR teams make formal recommendations to state governments on how to improve child safety and prevention efforts across the state. (For more information on CDR teams, see Chapter 2.)

OTHER RESPONSIBILITIES: TESTIFYING AND TRAINING

The ME may be required to testify regarding the autopsy findings in depositions, criminal trials, and other proceedings. MEs are considered expert witnesses, and they may be the key expert in certain legal proceedings in which forensic findings are, or could be, central to the case. Explaining complex scientific findings to a judge and jury who likely have little or no medical training requires particular specialized competencies (eg, excellent communication skills, objectivity, and poise).

The ME also plays an important role in educating forensic pathology fellows and other medical trainees (eg, child abuse pediatrics fellows). Speaking at multidisciplinary conferences or in other professional settings further helps to elucidate ways in which children die, and potentially, how to prevent future child deaths.

SUMMARY

The ME plays a critical role in child maltreatment investigations and unexplained childhood fatalities. As an integral member of a multidisciplinary team, the ME brings a unique set of skills, abilities, and insights to assist with one of the most difficult circumstances: the death of a child.

REFERENCES

1. Blau D, Clark S, Nolte K. Infectious disease surveillance by medical examiners and coroners. *Emerg Infect Dis*. 2013;19(5):821.

2. Palusci VJ; Council on Child Abuse and Neglect, Kay AJ, et al. Identifying child abuse fatalities during infancy. *Pediatrics*. 2019;144(3):e20192076. doi:10.1542/peds.2019-2076

3. Coroners don't need degrees to determine death. *Post Mortem: Death Investigations in America*. National Public Radio. February 2, 2011. https://www.npr.org/2011/02/02/133403760/coroners-dont-need-degrees-to-determine-death

4. Downs J, Harris, B. The role of coroners. In: Alexander R, ed. *Child Fatality Review: An Interdisciplinary Guide and Photographic Reference*. GW Medical; 2007:553-564.

5. Ernst M. The medicolegal death investigator. In: Alexander R, ed. *Child Fatality Review: An Interdisciplinary Guide and Photographic Reference*. GW Medical; 2007:543-552.

6. Willinger M, James LS, Catz C. Defining the sudden infant death syndrome (SIDS): deliberations of an expert panel convened by the National Institute of Child Health and Human Development. *Pediatr Pathol*. 1991;11(5):677-684.

7. Sudden unexpected infant death and sudden infant death syndrome, about SUID and SIDS. Centers for Disease Control and Prevention. Accessed December 28, 2020. https://www.cdc.gov/sids/about/index.htm

8. Lee CK, Lathrop SL. Child abuse related homicides in New Mexico: a 6 year retrospective review. *J Forensic Sciences*. 2010;55:100-103.

9. Sugar NF, Taylor JA, Feldman KW, Puget Sound Pediatric Research Network. Bruises in infants and toddlers: those who don't cruise rarely bruise. *Arch Pediatr Adolesc Med*. 1999;153(4):399-403.

10. Fox, S. Sentinel bruising and abusive injury. Pediatric EM Morsels. May 24, 2019. https://pedemmorsels.com/sentinel-bruising-abusive-injury

11. Pierce MC, Kaczor K, Aldridge S, O'Flynn J, Lorenz DJ. Bruising characteristics discriminating physical child abuse from accidental trauma. *Pediatrics*. 2010;125(1):67-74.

12. Adams JA, Farst KJ, Kellogg ND. Interpretation of medical findings in suspected child sexual abuse: an update for 2018. *J Pediatr Adolesc Gynecol*. 2017;31(3):225-231.

LEGAL ISSUES

The Honorable Anna-Kristie Morffi Marks

OBJECTIVES

After reviewing this chapter, the reader will be able to:

1. *Identify who must report child abuse and to whom they should report.*

2. *List what must be reported in child abuse and neglect cases.*

3. *Define the role of Child Protective Services (CPS) in child maltreatment cases.*

4. *Describe the course of litigation in child abuse and neglect cases.*

5. *Understand the rules of evidence as they apply in abuse cases.*

6. *Define the general provisions of state reporting statutes.*

CHILD PROTECTIVE SERVICES AND REPORTING STATUTES

The identification of abuse and neglect, the assessment of family social service needs, and the implementation of treatment programs and intervention strategies for abused children and their families are predominantly carried out by state and county CPS agencies. Typically, authorization for such interventions is found in state laws that establish and provide funding for these agencies as well as define the criteria for and mode of intervention. The primary purposes of CPS agencies are to protect and ensure the safety of children who are or who have been at risk of maltreatment and to provide services that prevent the risk of it in the future.

A report to the state's child abuse and neglect hotline, made either by a professional involved with the child or by a concerned nonmandated reporter, generally results in a referral to a CPS agency. Often, such a referral derives from a report taken by the local police. Child abuse and neglect reporting laws dictate the manner in which referrals are made to CPS agencies and how the agencies are to respond to such referrals. These laws govern the central registries that maintain information regarding cases previously investigated by CPS agencies, and they often define the relationship between the CPS agency, the court, and law enforcement agencies.

All states, including the United States' territories, have each enacted their own child abuse and neglect reporting legislation. As a result, there is a lack of uniformity in statutory language and the laws' effect. In particular, the statutes vary in their precise definition of child abuse or neglect as well in the standards and procedures used for reporting suspected cases. All of the state statutes, however, share a common purpose and tend to follow a similar format based on the federally mandated requirements.

The purpose of every child abuse and neglect reporting statute is to protect the child from additional physical and mental injury. Accordingly, statutes are written to encourage and facilitate reporting of suspected abuse or neglect. These statutes are designed to promote early identification of a child in peril in order to swiftly begin a thorough investigation of alleged abuse or neglect and initiate a response when protective measures and/or treatment are warranted.

Every state reporting statute contains essentially the same elements, including: (1) what must be reported (ie, reportable conditions/definition of child abuse or neglect), (2) who must or may report, (3) when a report must be made, (4) reporting procedures, (5) the existence and operation of a central registry, (6) rules regarding protective custody, (7) immunity for good faith reporters, (8) the abrogation of certain privileged communication rights that might otherwise apply, and (9) sanctions for failure to report. In addition, many child abuse reporting statutes allow the taking of photographs or x-rays of the child when physical abuse is suspected, even in the absence of parental consent.

WHO MUST REPORT WHAT TO WHOM
Each state's reporting statute designates who is required to report suspected child abuse and neglect. These individuals often include professionals such as physicians, health care employees, educators, and law enforcement personnel. Many states, though, have an even broader base of mandated reporters, which includes professionals such as coroners, funeral home directors, dentists, probation officers, social workers, or other persons responsible for the care of children. Approximately 18 states, however, require "any person" to report suspected child abuse and neglect. In addition, the majority of state reporting statutes also provide guidelines for permissive reporting by nonmandated reporters.

Each state statute specifies at least 1 agency to receive reports of suspected child abuse and neglect. Traditionally, 4 different agencies have served as potential recipients for child abuse reports: social service agencies, police departments, health departments, and the courts.

WHAT MUST BE REPORTED
Like mentioned above, every state's reporting statute requires that mandated reporters disclose any suspected child abuse and neglect. Each state, however, defines child abuse and neglect differently; therefore, reportable conditions vary among the states. In general, reportable conditions include: nonaccidental physical injury, neglect, sexual abuse, and/or emotional abuse.

WHEN MUST A REPORT BE MADE
Most state statutes require reporters to make an immediate oral report of suspected abuse or neglect by telephone, followed shortly thereafter by a written report, to the appropriate state agency. This procedure facilitates an immediate investigatory response by the CPS agency, ensuring that the child is protected. It also establishes a permanent record of the alleged incident. The degree of suspicion a reporter must reach before making a report is set out in the reporting statute and likewise varies from state to state. The first child abuse reporting statutes provided guidelines for a report to be made when there was "reason to believe" that a child had been abused. Many states have since expanded that requirement and now use language such as when one has "cause to believe" or "reasonable cause to suspect" that a "child has been or may be subjected to abuse or neglect or observes a child being subjected to conditions or circumstances which would reasonably result in abuse or neglect." Practically, "cause to believe" and "reasonable cause to suspect" have similar meanings for reporting purposes. As will be noted below, however, there may be a distinction in cases where civil liability for failure to report is an issue.

REPORTING PROCEDURES
Most states have designated the department of social services, or a division within that department, as the appropriate agency to receive reports of suspected child abuse and neglect. Some states designate reporting only to the department of social services, while others designate reporting to 2 or more agencies (eg, the police department and the department of social services), but these states generally require that all reports ultimately flow into the department of social services. A few states,

however, permit the reporting to 2 or more agencies without requiring the coordination of information by any agency.

In many states, the reporting statute specifies what information must to be included in the report. In other states, the receiving agency determines on a case-by-case basis what information is required. Typically, the required information is: name, age, address, present location of the child, type and extent of the injuries, name and address of the parent(s) or caretaker(s) if known, and any other information that the reporter believes might be relevant. Most states require a mandated reporter to divulge their name and position but allow for a permissive reporter to remain anonymous. Reporting statutes also generally prescribe the time within which the CPS agency must initiate its investigation. In most instances, this is within 24 hours of the receipt of a report.

CENTRAL REGISTRIES

Nearly every state has established a central registry of child protection cases, which is where reports received by their child abuse hotline are recorded. Central registry records usually contain additional case information such as prior reports of child abuse and neglect, CPS case outcomes, treatment plans, and final dispositions at the CPS level. Because central registry records contain highly private data about individuals and families, state laws generally deem them confidential and regulate their disclosure.

Three general statutory approaches govern record accessibility: (1) only individuals within a CPS agency may have access, (2) the CPS agency may issue regulations authorizing access by certain persons outside of the agency, or (3) state law may enumerate precisely which persons may have access. This third approach is most prevalent today. Those who typically have access to the records are law enforcement personnel investigating a report of child maltreatment, the treating physician, the CPS agency, the court, and/or the persons conducting bona fide research. In addition, the child's attorney or guardian ad litem is generally permitted to review registry records in instances when the CPS agency or law enforcement personnel refers the case to court and court involvement ensues. Registry information is often available for purposes such as screening applicants for licenses to establish childcare facilities, agencies/services/applicants for employment, or volunteer work with such operations or with schools.

PROTECTIVE CUSTODY

Nearly every state authorizes certain categories of individuals to take a child into protective custody if the individual concludes that there is "an imminent danger to the child's life or health" or if the child's health and wellbeing would be "seriously endangered" if they remained with or were released to their parent or other caretaker.[1] The child abuse reporting statutes designate who may take the child into custody, when, and under what circumstances. Depending on the particular statute, such individuals may include 1 or more of the following: police officers, physicians, juvenile or probation officers, and/or CPS professionals.[2]

Some states require a court order, at least over the telephone if not in writing, before taking the child into custody against the parent's or caretaker's wishes. Other states directly authorize protective custody, provided that written notice or another document is filed with the juvenile court within 24 to 48 hours after the action is taken. In either case, a custody hearing will typically be held in court within a short period of time to review the initial decision of holding the child.

IMMUNITY FOR GOOD FAITH REPORTERS

Individuals may be reluctant to report suspected child abuse. Potential reporters may fear that the suspected perpetrator will bring a lawsuit against them if the abuse is unconfirmed. To encourage reporting and alleviate this fear, every state's reporting statute extends some type of immunity for civil and criminal liability and to persons making reports.[3] Although such immunity provisions may not completely insulate the reporter from a lawsuit (ie, they cannot prevent the filing of an action against a reporter), they can make the successful litigation of such suits nearly impossible.

ABROGATION OF PRIVILEGED COMMUNICATIONS

Certain professionals owe their patients or clients the duty of confidentiality. This duty is incurred by virtue of the ethical obligations which the individual undertakes upon becoming a professional of their field and adopting the standards of that profession. Ordinarily, any breach of this obligation will lead to a malpractice suit against the professional in which money might be awarded to the patient or client as compensation for damages sustained as a result of the breach of confidentiality. If the disclosure is mandated by a state statute, however, as in the instance of child abuse, no liability will result. Moreover, in such instances, the failure to make the disclosure, even in the face of an otherwise existing obligation of confidentiality, may, in fact, result in liability.

In addition to this obligation of confidentiality, certain professional communications are protected by a judicially or legislatively created testimonial privilege. Generally, a privilege operates to exclude information obtained in the course of a particular relationship from being presented as evidence at judicial proceedings. The most common types of privileged communications are: doctor-patient, husband-wife, attorney-client, social worker-client, and priest-penitent. States differ, however, as to which communications are protected by testimonial privilege. Most states abrogate all types of privileged communications in a child abuse case. The most common exception, however, is the attorney-client privilege.

Mandated reporters must report suspected abuse or neglect, regardless of whether the abuse or neglect became apparent as a result of a confidential communication with the patient or client. Also, the professional must testify in court when subpoenaed in child protection cases. In many jurisdictions, this requirement to testify may also exist in criminal cases and in child custody cases in which allegations of child abuse are involved in the report. Failure to testify when a judge orders that the testimony be given is likely to result in the judge holding the witness in contempt and ordering a fine and/or incarceration.

CRIMINAL SANCTIONS FOR FAILURE TO REPORT

Most states have provisions in their reporting statutes that make it a crime for a mandated reporter to knowingly fail to report suspected child abuse. Almost all of these statutes classify the offense as a misdemeanor and specify a maximum fine and/or jail sentence. Although criminal prosecutions for failure to report are rare, courts have ruled that physicians, including psychiatrists, may be subject to criminal penalty under the child abuse statute for failure to report suspected child abuse.[4] The inclusion of a penalty provision serves a useful function for reluctant professionals because they can then explain to the child's family or caretakers that it is a crime for them not to make the report.

INVESTIGATIVE PURPOSES AND PROCEDURES

Reporting statutes often detail the purpose of the investigation. Generally, the goal is to evaluate the nature, extent, and cause of the child's abuse or neglect and to identify the person responsible. Efforts are also made to ascertain the names and physical conditions of other children in the home, the nature of the home environment, and the relationship of the child to the parents or other caretakers.

The child abuse or neglect investigation consists of a series of interviews. An investigative caseworker typically begins the process by interviewing the individual who initially made the hotline report in order to confirm the information originally provided and to obtain additional details. Often, the child is the next person who is interviewed, preferably in a neutral setting. The parents/caregivers are also interviewed, typically during a home visit. Thereafter, other persons named in the report who may have relevant information (eg, teachers, physicians, neighbors, relatives) are questioned.

The objectives of CPS when responding to a report of child maltreatment are distinct from the objectives of the criminal justice system; yet, as noted, law enforcement personnel may be contacted by the CPS worker during the investigatory stage or they may already be otherwise involved in the investigation. This is true in cases involving physical abuse where there is a reason to believe that the parents/caregivers are or may likely be resistant to CPS intervention or if the CPS caseworker is concerned for their own safety. State law provides the authority for CPS home visits, either expressly or through implication, but if individuals refuse to cooperate, a warrant or court order may be needed to gain access to a home. In addition, many state statutes, regulations, or case laws authorize CPS or law enforcement investigators to conduct examinations of the child or to refer the child for evaluation by medical personnel.

VALIDATION OF REPORTS

As stated in the preceding discussion of reporting procedures, each state has enacted legislation prescribing criteria for case follow-up, which generally requires an investigation within a limited period of time. The primary aim of the investigation is to determine the validity of the report. If the case is ***substantiated***, ***founded***, or ***indicated*** a decision must be made on how to proceed. If the child is not in the protective custody of a physician, the police, or the court at the time of the investigation, the CPS investigator must determine if there is imminent risk of harm to the child that would warrant the child's immediate removal from the home. If such action is needed, the police or the court may be contacted to facilitate this removal. If the available evidence is insufficient to merit a finding of abuse or neglect, or if the investigation could not be completed, the case may be deemed ***unsubstantiated*** or ***unfounded***. If no additional reports are made, the case may then be closed and all references to the report and case will be deleted from the central registry within a designated period of time.[5] Since central registries involve state collection of potentially inflammatory personal information, this gives rise to constitutional concerns regarding the rights to privacy and due process. Accordingly, many states have enacted procedures, by statute or state regulation, for the expungement of registry records. Expungement of records is based either on the child turning a certain age, passage of a designated period of time since services were terminated, or upon a finding by the CPS agency making the report unsubstantiated. In some states, individuals may formally challenge information contained in the registry through administrative or court procedures for the expungement or modification of records.

TREATMENT AND REFERRAL OPTIONS

If a hotline referral is substantiated, a CPS caseworker, who may or may not have been involved in the initial investigation of the report, is usually assigned to the case. The caseworker develops a treatment plan and presents it to the family, seeking the family's voluntary acceptance of their recommended services. If the parent or caregiver does not cooperate with the CPS agency, or if such voluntary treatment will not adequately protect the child, the investigative or treatment caseworker will request that a juvenile or probation officer file an abuse or neglect petition with the juvenile or family court or file such an action themselves. Such an action will seek court intervention with the child and their family. Intervention may include temporary removal of the child from the home, court-ordered treatment, or, in some circumstances, termination of parental rights. It is in situations such as these that the precise language of the reporting statute may be of great legal significance.

ADDITIONAL CAUSES OF ACTION BASED ON FAILURES TO PROTECT THE CHILD AND RELATED DEFENSES

In situations involving state-employed child protection workers in which there was a resulted death or additional serious injury to the child, the child and a parent or caregiver may bring an action alleging that the public employees should have taken various steps in order to protect the child. These lawsuits often allege a failure to accept reports for investigation, a failure to adequately investigate reports, a failure to remove the child from the home, a failure to protect the child after return to the home, foster care, or a childcare facility, or a failure to provide services leading to the return of the child. These actions are also typically brought under state tort law.

THE LITIGATION OF CHILD ABUSE AND NEGLECT CASES

JUVENILE COURT

The role of the juvenile or family court in child abuse cases is as follows:

— To protect the child from further injury

— To provide a fair and impartial hearing on the allegations in the petition

— To consider recommendations of CPS and other social services agencies

— To implement a treatment plan for the child and/or the parent(s)/caregiver(s) when appropriate

— To protect the constitutional rights of both the child and the parent(s)/caregiver(s)

The function of the juvenile or family court system is not to punish but rather to work closely with the social service agencies in order to create a treatment plan that is designed to protect the child. Generally, the court seeks to improve the family situation in order to keep the family intact, unless the child has suffered serious harm and would continue to be endangered if allowed to remain within that family.

The participants in the juvenile court process include: the judge, the petitioner, the child, the parent(s)/caregiver(s), the attorney for the petitioner, the attorney for the parent(s)/caregiver(s), and a representative for the child. Some of the court proceedings include custody hearings, adjudicatory hearings, and dispositional hearings.

CRIMINAL COURT

The prosecution of individuals accused of crimes perpetrated against children has increased in recent decades, particularly in the area of child sexual abuse. This increase is due, in part, to advances made in identifying physically and sexually abused children and, in part, to the relaxation of evidentiary rules relating to victim competency, in-court testimony, and certain out-of-court statements. Although the juvenile court's involvement in these cases is based on the state's role as *parens patriae* (ie, the legal protector of citizens unable to protect themselves), the criminal justice system's involvement is exercised under the state's police power, which authorizes official action in preventing identified harms to society. The criminal justice system includes law enforcement investigations, criminal prosecutions, and sentencing proceedings. The substantive criminal law defines what conduct is considered criminal, as well as provides the punishment to be imposed on an adjudication or finding of guilt.

PROCEDURAL AND EVIDENTIARY RULES

Evidentiary rules control the extent to which professional privileges will limit the amount of information available to a court. Although most state reporting statutes seem to abrogate these privileges in child custody situations involving known or suspected child abuse or neglect, the precise language of the statutory provision that abrogates the privilege in a given state and possible judicial interpretations of that language could still affect whether or not related evidence is deemed admissible.

CUSTODIAL CONSIDERATIONS

When custody is contested, the judge must choose among various alternative arrangements, allocating between the 2 parents/caregivers the rights and obligations relating to the child that was formerly shared by them. Foremost in this analysis is always what custodial arrangement would be in "the best interests of the child." In cases where child maltreatment is alleged, the court necessarily seeks to determine the truth of the accusations. When the allegations are substantiated, the judge should choose a custody arrangement that will maximize the child's safety, which is paramount.

REVIEW AND MODIFICATION

Custody decisions are generally viewed as matters best left to the sound discretion of the trial court due to the fact-sensitive nature of the determinations, combined with the general lack of firm guidelines controlling "the best interests of the child" analysis. The wide latitude traditionally afforded to a trial court allows for a necessarily individualized case-by-case decision. It does, however, limit the scope of review of an appellate court to that of reversal only for an "abuse of discretion."[6] Thus, on appeal, a higher court generally will not re-evaluate the facts to determine whether, in its own view, a finding of child abuse perpetrated by the accused should have been made.

EVIDENTIARY ISSUES

The ***law of evidence*** is the system of rules and standards that regulates the admission of proof in a court proceeding.[7] In response to efforts to introduce various types of evidence, in the nature of both testimony and physical exhibits (sometimes called "real" evidence), objections may be made by opposing counsel. The trial judge must then rule on these objections and determine what actual evidence the finder of fact (eg, the jury in criminal cases or the judge in juvenile or family court cases) will be allowed to consider in the proceeding. The judge relies on established rules that are part of the law of evidence in making these determinations.

General rules of evidence may affect virtually any question that is asked of a witness during the trial. Particularly unique and difficult evidentiary issues do arise in cases involving child abuse and neglect, and these issues may include: the possible use of circumstantial evidence, the competency of child witnesses, the use of hearsay testimony, limits regarding the scope of admissible expert testimony, and the use of various types of demonstrative evidence such as photographs.

Generally, the applicable rules of evidence in criminal child abuse prosecutions, civil juvenile court child protection proceedings, and child custody cases are the same. The rules may be somewhat relaxed in noncriminal proceedings in juvenile court or family court cases because a judge, rather than a jury, is the fact finder and has been trained to ignore inadmissible evidence while making their determination.

DIRECT AND CIRCUMSTANTIAL EVIDENCE

Often, child abuse does not yield a great deal of evidence that, under the rules of evidence, would be admissible in any of the trials or hearings related to child abuse. Most cases of child abuse occur in the child's home, and often the only people present are the child and the perpetrator. Even when others are present at the time of the incident, in many instances it is a member of the immediate family, such as a spouse, who may be unwilling to testify or to testify truthfully or a young child who is too immature to take the witness stand. Additionally, the victim is frequently too young or immature to testify. Even if the child is mature enough, however, they may be reluctant to do so or will change or recant their story. The alleged perpetrator is typically a trusted member of the family who contends that the child's injuries were accidental; therefore, direct evidence is usually sparse or nonexistent.

Direct evidence is evidence which, if believed, resolves the matter in issue.[7] Most of the available evidence in child abuse cases is circumstantial. ***Circumstantial evidence*** is evidence that is not based on actual personal knowledge or observation of the facts or events in controversy. Rather, it is based on facts from which deductions may be drawn, showing indirectly that certain events did take place or that certain other facts sought to be proved are true. However, circumstantial evidence, even if believed, does not resolve the matter at hand. Additional reasoning must be applied to reach the proposition to which it is directed.[7]

For example, a witness' testimony claiming that he saw X beat a child with a belt is direct evidence of whether X did, indeed, beat the child. Testimony that the child had belt marks on his back and legs, that the child was in X's custody, and that no one else had access to the child during the time when the marks were acquired would be strong circumstantial evidence that X beat the child. A case of child abuse may be proven entirely by circumstantial evidence, but there still must be sufficient evidence to convince the trier of fact.

COMPETENCY

An individual must be competent to testify as a witness at any trial or hearing. Generally, the courts assess a child's competency through 3 factors: (1) the child's ability to communicate the event, (2) the child's ability to observe and recall an event, and (3) the child's understanding of the necessity to speak the truth.

Historically, courts and legislatures created presumptions, depending on age, regarding the competency of children to testify. More recently, however, the trend has been to presume that all witnesses are competent to testify and to resolve doubt as to the credibility of the witness in favor of allowing the testimony and having the trier of fact decide what weight to give that testimony. A party may still challenge a child's competency, and if the trial judge finds that the witness did not meet one of the criteria listed above, the judge may prohibit the testimony.

HEARSAY

In general, a witness can only testify to those facts about which they have personal knowledge. The witness may not testify to what others have said in an out-of-court or extra-judicial statement to prove the truth of the matter asserted. Such secondhand information is called ***hearsay***.[7] Hearsay evidence is usually inadmissible in a judicial proceeding and is excluded to prevent the introduction of statements made by out-of-court declarants whose statements were not made under oath and whose credibility cannot be evaluated by the jury.[7]

There are, however, certain recognized exceptions to the hearsay rule. Each of these exceptions has been recognized in some or all jurisdictions. The exceptions typically have been created when the situation and the circumstances surrounding the declarant's statement increase the reliability of the out-of-court statement and thereby make the statement more trustworthy.[7] For such statements to be admissible, they must meet the jurisdiction's requirements for that particular hearsay exception and, in criminal cases, not violate the Confrontation Clause of the Constitution of the United States. A number of the recognized exceptions to the hearsay rule are important in child abuse and neglect cases. These exceptions are found under Section 803 of the Federal Rules of Evidence, which most states have adopted.

Excited Utterances and Statements of Physical and Mental Conditions

One recognized hearsay exception is that of excited utterances. This exception allows for the admission of nonreflective statements regarding a startling event made while the declarant is still in a state of excitement. For example, a statement made by a child to a neighbor or the police that her mother beat her with a belt may be admissible if the court finds that the statement was made while the child was still under the stress of excitement caused by the beating and that the statement was impulsive and spontaneous rather than a product of reflective thought.

A related exception that is recognized in most jurisdictions is that of statements made to anyone regarding their then-existing physical conditions, including pain or other physical sensations. These are admissible to prove the truth of the statement (ie, to prove that the physical condition or pain existed at the time the statement was made). Thus, for example, a statement made by a child to their mother, while pointing to a genital area saying that "it hurts," could be admissible under this exception.

Similarly, most jurisdictions admit statements of the declarant's then-existing state of mind or emotion. Thus, for example, in a child custody litigation incident of divorce, a child's statement to another individual regarding affection for or dislike of a parent/caregiver will be admissible. Statements indicating fear of an abusive parent/caregiver may also be admitted.

Statements for Medical Diagnosis
In most jurisdictions, there is a separate recognized exception that authorizes the admission of statements made for purposes of medical diagnosis and treatment. Statements admissible under this exception may pertain to present or past conditions of the victim, if they are made to a physician or the physician's agent, such as a nurse or technician. Such statements are admissible on the assumption that one generally does not fabricate statements to health care providers because the success of the patient's treatment depends on the accuracy of the information provided to medical personnel.

Some courts will also admit statements that refer to the cause of the condition for which the declarant is seeking treatment if the statements are reasonably pertinent to the diagnosis and are made in connection with the treatment. In a child abuse situation, a number of courts have reasoned that because the treatment of child abuse includes removing the child from the abusive setting, the doctor should attempt to ascertain the identity of the abuser. Therefore, a child's statement to a physician, in the effect of "Daddy hurt me," may be admitted into evidence.

Present Sense Impressions
A few jurisdictions recognize an exception for "present sense impressions." *Present sense impressions* are statements describing or explaining an event or condition that are made while the declarant was perceiving the event or condition or immediately thereafter. For example, if a child was rescued while the abuse was taking place and immediately began to describe what had occurred to the rescuer, their statement may be admitted.

Admissions by Parties
Another recognized non-hearsay rule is when the out-of-court statement is that of a party to the litigation and is relevant to the party's defense. For example, a parent-perpetrator may tell a neighbor, "I beat my child because he wet his pants." In a criminal case against the parent, the neighbor could testify to this statement; however, its admission in a juvenile court proceeding may depend on whether the parent is considered a party under the state's juvenile court rules.

Business and Medical Records
Another exception to the hearsay rule allows for the introduction of business records, which generally includes medical records. When business records are used to prove the truth of their contents, this constitutes hearsay. Such records, however, often are admitted under a recognized exception to the hearsay rule when the records are kept by a business as part of its regular operation. The theory of this admittance is that if the business itself will rely on the accuracy of such records in carrying out its operations, a court should do likewise. For the record to be admitted, though, there must be foundational testimony to the effect that the entry to the records was made

accurately and promptly, that it was done in the course of usual business activity, and that the person recording the information had firsthand knowledge of the matter.

In most instances, medical records, including any laboratory and/or x-ray findings, may be admissible as substantive evidence of the child's diagnosis, condition, and medical history under the business records exception to the hearsay rule. Medical records may also be used to refresh the physician's memory regarding the specific case when the physician is testifying at trial or giving evidence in a deposition. This refreshment use is appropriate regardless of whether or not the record is otherwise admissible as a business record.

Many courts are reluctant, however, to admit prognostic statements or statements concerning the cause of a condition that are contained in the medical record unless the doctor who wrote the statement is available for cross-examination or the statement was based on objective data rather than data requiring speculation. For example, it would probably not be necessary to have a radiologist testify in court that the child has a spiral fracture of the femur, but instead, the record would be admissible to show that the child had the spiral fracture. Conversely, a doctor's statement that the spiral fracture of the femur was caused by child abuse, rather than by an accidental fall, would probably not be admitted into evidence unless the doctor was available for cross-examination.

Residual Exception
Some jurisdictions have recognized a so-called "residual" exception to the hearsay rule. This exception, under limited situations, permits the receipt of "reliable" hearsay evidence that does not fit into an established exception, as long as the statement has "equivalent circumstantial guarantees of trustworthiness" to the recognized exceptions. Courts have sometimes relied on this exception in litigation involving children.

Sexual Abuse Exception
A number of jurisdictions, either legislatively or by judicial decision, have created a hearsay exception, sometimes referred to as the "tender years" exception, that authorizes the admission of out-of-court statements by children under a certain age regarding sexual abuse.[7] Often the sexual abuse hearsay exception's applicability is limited to criminal and/or juvenile court proceedings. The time, content, and circumstances of the statement must provide sufficient guarantees of trustworthiness. In addition, the child must either testify at the hearing or be "unavailable." When unavailable, there must be additional corroborative evidence of the act that is the subject of the child's statement. These statutes allow a parent/caregiver, doctor, or other individual to whom a child has made a statement regarding sexual abuse to, testify to the child's description of what occurred, regardless of whether the statement otherwise meets the requirements of another hearsay exception.

Videotaping Statutes
Some state legislatures have passed statutes permitting a child's testimony to be preserved on videotape for presentation to a jury, thus enabling the child to avoid repeated appearances in court.[7] If certain requirements are met, the statutes exempt the ban on hearsay in cases when an audiovisual recorded statement of a child victim or witness describes an act of sexual abuse or physical violence. For this to happen, the court must find that (1) the minor will suffer emotional or psychological stress if required to testify in open court, (2) the time, content, and circumstances of the statement provide sufficient guarantees of trustworthiness, and (3) certain other procedural requirements were met. Generally, the presence of the judge, the accused, or the counsel is not required at the taping, and while any person can conduct the interview, many of these interviews are conducted by child interview specialists. Before the statement is admitted, and upon the defendant's request, the court will provide further questioning of the minor.

In addition, these statutes authorize the presentation of the evidence of the child's statement (either by audiovisual recorded deposition or by closed circuit television) as the equivalent of testimony. Such statutes specify who is to be present at the recording of the child's statement and authorize the exclusion of a party, if found that their presence may cause severe emotional or psychological distress to the child. The use of such a recording is permitted, provided the defendant can observe and hear the testimony and can consult with their lawyer.

Confrontation Clause Issues

Although the rules regarding hearsay and its exceptions are generally applicable in juvenile, criminal, and divorce cases, particular note should be made of the interplay between these hearsay rules and a criminal defendant's rights under the Confrontation Clause of the Sixth Amendment to the Constitution of the United States. As noted in the discussion of criminal trials, as well as in the discussion of hearsay, state legislatures and trial courts have endeavored to reduce the trauma a child might sustain from testifying in a criminal trial. Such protective measures, however, may violate the Confrontation Clause.[8]

EXPERT TESTIMONY

Generally, a **witness** is only permitted to testify to factual matters and may not offer an opinion or conclusion regarding the meaning of those facts. An **expert witness**, however, is allowed to give opinions in areas related to their expertise when and if the judge determines that such testimony is beyond the common knowledge of the trier of fact and will aid the trier of fact in deciding the issues of the case.[7] To qualify as an expert, the witness will be required to state facts about their education and experience. The opposing attorney or the judge may ask additional questions regarding the witness' expertise. The trial judge is given great discretion in deciding whether the witness qualifies as an expert.

In general, physicians and other licensed or certified health care professionals have sufficient training and experience to express a medical opinion that will help the judge or jury understand the medical aspects of the case. Therefore, in most situations, an individual with a medical degree will qualify as an expert witness. There is no requirement for sub-specialization. The weight that the fact finder, be it a judge or a jury, gives to the physician's testimony may, however, be affected by factors such as board certification in the particular area involved, experience, publications, and/or the clarity of the witness' presentation concerning the pertinent condition.

DEMONSTRATIVE EVIDENCE

Demonstrative evidence consists of things (eg, photographs, medical illustrations or diagrams of the child's injuries, x-rays, etc.), rather than the assertions made by witnesses about said things. In child abuse cases, demonstrative evidence frequently helps the trier of fact understand a particular issue.

PHOTOGRAPHS, ILLUSTRATIONS, AND X-RAYS

Generally, demonstrative evidence will be admitted if a proper foundation is laid. Specifically, it must be shown that the demonstrative object is a fair and accurate representation of the thing it purports to represent or illustrate. For example, if a physician testifies about a child's bruises and cuts observed in the hospital and then is shown a picture of the child taken at approximately the same time the doctor examined the child, the doctor will be allowed to testify that the photograph is a "true and accurate representation" of what they saw. Consequently, the photograph can then be admitted into evidence and shown to the trier of fact. Similarly, illustrations that indicate the location of injuries may be admitted if the proper foundation is laid.

In a criminal prosecution for child abuse, admission of photographs of the child's injuries is left to the discretion of the judge because such photographs may inflame and prejudice a jury. The judge must balance the probative value of the pictures against their prejudicial effect in ruling on admissibility.

Typically, the child's x-rays will be admitted into evidence if accompanied by testimony explaining their relevance. X-rays may reveal certain types of fractures that, when found in a young child, are indicative of child abuse rather than accidental injury. For example, posterior rib fractures in different stages of healing in a young child may be highly suggestive of physical abuse. Conversely, an x-ray may indicate an accident rather than child abuse. A fractured clavicle accompanied by bruises on the arms may be indicative of an accidental fall.

SUMMARY

State and county CPS agencies, whose primary purpose is to ensure the health and safety of children, carry out the identification of child maltreatment, assess a family's social service needs, and implement treatment programs and intervention strategies in order to prevent maltreatment in the future. Each state has requirements for who, when, and what must be reported by a mandated reporter. Furthermore, this chapter has covered the clearly defined court procedures for child abuse cases, including what is and is not admissible as evidence in court, what witnesses are allowed to testify about, and common hearsay exceptions.

REFERENCES

1. Meriwether M. Child abuse reporting laws: time for a change. *Fam L Q.* 1986;20(2):141-171.

2. US Department of Health and Human Services; Administration for Children and Families; Children's Bureau. Mandatory reporters of child abuse and neglect. April 2019. Accessed November 30, 2021. https://www.childwelfare.gov/pubPDFs/manda.pdf

3. Fraser BG. A glance at the past, a gaze at the present, a glimpse at the future: a critical analysis of the development of child abuse reporting statutes. *Chi Kent L.* 1978;54(3):641.

4. *Groff v State*, 390 SO2d 361 (Fla Dist Ct App 1980).

5. Iverson T, Segal M. *Child Abuse and Neglect: An Information and Reference Guide.* Garland Publishing, Inc; 1990.

6. *TB v LRM*, 567 PA 222 (Pa 2001).

7. McCormick C. *Hornbook on the Law of Evidence,* 7th ed. West Publishing Co; 2014.

8. *Crawford v Washington*, 541 US 36 (2004).

TESTIFYING

Randell Alexander, MD, PhD

OBJECTIVES
After reviewing this chapter, the reader will be able to:

1. *Compare and contrast the legal environment with the medical or social services environment.*

2. *Understand how to prepare a case for court.*

3. *Determine the role of the witness.*

4. *Explain preparation for testifying.*

5. *Describe the elements of giving testimony.*

6. *List cross-examination strategies and how to respond to them if necessary.*

7. *Discuss levels of certainty.*

OVERVIEW OF MEDICAL AND LEGAL ENVIRONMENTS
Medical professionals are accustomed to taking a team approach in order to achieve the highest level of well-being for their patients. The ultimate goal of this approach is to correctly identify their patients' problems and then to treat or cure them. The legal system, however, presents an adversarial situation, in which each lawyer attempts to prove the merits of their own case while simultaneously discrediting the opposite view.

Lawyers ensure justice by protecting the legal process and the rights of the individuals they represent. Judges are most concerned with procedure and with ensuring that the case will be upheld under the scrutiny of the courts of appeal. If there is a jury, it is largely made up of individuals who tend to be unversed in technical medical matters. Therefore, the jury sees the case through the interpretative efforts of the witnesses and lawyers.

Most child protection cases are heard in juvenile court, where there is no jury, and decisions are made solely by the judge. Judges serving in these cases are generally sensitive to children's issues and will make decisions based on what will achieve the best possible result for the child while still protecting the rights of the family. However, trials consist of 2 sides presenting admissible evidence. Oftentimes, the better prepared, better qualified, and most articulate lawyer wins, whether justice is served or not.

DOCUMENTATION
Preparation for court *actually* begins with each clinical encounter. Remember, there is always the potential for every medical encounter to result in a court case, no matter how innocuous the encounter seems at the time. It should also be noted that the odds for a court case are considerably higher when child abuse is suspected; therefore, documentation is key.

Clarity while obtaining and documenting a medical history is always helpful, but particularly so when details will later be scrutinized in court. The elements of clarity include:

— **Not being influenced by the family:** Stay objective. Focus on the injuries and/or the history of harm. Remember, it is a potential bias to debate whether or not the parent seems nice; even seemingly nice people can commit terrible abuse. Conversely, adults who present poorly should not be judged by appearance, but by actions.

— **Taking good notes:** Criminal cases may arise months or years later. Memories of details fade. Document quotations when possible. Use diagrams and photographs, or both, of injuries. Avoid being cursory. A year later, documentation of "multiple" bruises will not be as substantial as having actually counted "67" bruises. Measure, describe color of injuries, the demeanor of the child, any odors, general habitus, etc. Be sure to also retain any notes that were kept separate from medical records.

— **Talking to each caregiver and the child separately, if possible:** Do not try to reconcile the histories if different, just document what was actually said.

— **Not hedging the diagnosis by saying "suspected abuse" if "abuse" is the diagnosis:** At a trial, it is fair for a lawyer to ask what information was reviewed in the interim to change the opinion from "suspected abuse" to "abuse." Mirroring any other medical condition, the categories for documentation are typically "no evidence of abuse," "indeterminate," or "positive" for abuse.

— **Reporting cases of suspected or diagnosed abuse to Child Protective Services (CPS) as required by law:** Assist both CPS and law enforcement by describing not only the concern, but what recommendations you are making as a professional.

— **Treating any telephone contact, text, email, or other communication as liable to arise in court:** It is important to stay professional at all times.

Preparing for the Case

When someone is called upon to testify, initial contact will be made by a lawyer or their office via an email, a phone call, or a subpoena. Testimony in court is usually on behalf of the prosecution. A discovery deposition by the opposing side may be scheduled. The purpose of this deposition is to determine what the proposed testimony may be, so discuss the case with the prosecutor prior to it. Scheduling should be negotiated. Depositions are under oath. While there is no judge or jury, a transcript and, at times, a video recording, is generated. Understanding that there will be documentation of words and/or actions, one should conduct themselves as they would in court. Occasionally there can be an evidentiary deposition whereby the deposition (transcribed or video) is used in the actual trial instead of the live witness. This can occur when the witness is unavailable at the time of the trial (eg, out of the country).

For the trial itself, when a subpoena instructs a call to the Victim Witness office, call the prosecutor directly instead. These are the items to discuss with the prosecutor:

— **Your role:** Are you a fact witness or an expert witness? A fact witness is someone who merely describes what happened (eg, "that is my signature") and supplies no opinion. An expert witness is an individual who knows more than the average person, thereby giving them the ability to assist the jury or judge (ie, virtually all doctors). They can supply opinions about what the facts mean.

— **Any fees, if applicable:** An expert witness typically charges for their time.

— **Your exact expectations for testifying:** What records will you need to review in advance? How will you obtain these records?

— **Exactly what time you are needed:** Typically, when a subpoena on a criminal case states "Monday morning at 9:00 AM," that is not the actual time at which you are needed, but when a jury is picked. Ask if you may be contacted just before you are needed in order to avoid waiting. The time may need to be negotiated, if necessary or possible.

— **Parking and where to go upon arrival:** It should be more specific than "the courthouse," so ask which floor, which room, and where to wait. It is best to arrive 30 minutes in advance in case of last-minute delays (eg, parking, traffic, getting lost, etc.). Occasionally, a witness will finish earlier than expected, and you may go on the stand sooner, so it is important to be early.

To best prepare for a case, keep the following information in mind:

— Send a curriculum vitae (CV) in advance or bring one along in case your credentials are needed.

— Remember, any notes that you take up to the witness stand can be reviewed by the opposing attorney, so discuss what is advisable to write in advance. Typically, you do not own the medical record and cannot re-disseminate it. The attorneys will furnish records for review during testimony if they are thought to be important.

— Read the case history and other materials carefully and thoroughly before your court appearance.

— Review any deposition that you may have given previously. By doing so, you will avoid the embarrassment of contradicting previous testimony without being able to offer a valid explanation for the difference.

— In preparation for testimony, read textbooks and key references. You may be questioned regarding an unfamiliar reference, and you should ask to see it while on the stand. Especially note the publication date and journal source when gauging your response. Often, saying that you do not know those sources will stop that line of questioning.

— If you are being called as an expert witness, it is important to appear professional. A coat and tie, or a conservative suit or dress, is preferred. Keep your tone, attitude, and reactions consistent throughout your testimony. It is best to be controlled, polite, humble, serious, and patient. A poor impression is left by those who are defensive, overbearing, tentative, smug, clever, amusing, or entertaining. In addition, the way you deliver information is extremely important. Your role, and what gives the best impression, is to present yourself as a teacher.

Testimony

As stated earlier, the expert witness is there to provide facts and supply opinions. Communicating an accurate, unbiased depiction of these opinions is key. The expert witness is not there to "take sides."

While appearing as an expert witness, remember the following:

— Avoid technical jargon as much as possible, but do not be condescending.

— If you provide any long answers, speak directly to the jury or judge.

— Listen carefully to each question. Think a few seconds before answering.

— Stop if an objection is made and wait until the judge rules. Ask to have the question repeated if you are not absolutely certain what it was.

— You cannot object to a question or refuse to answer. If pressured to say "yes" or "no," when that is inappropriate, try to say that such a simple answer could be misleading.

— The lawyer, tactically, may also ask several simple questions requiring a "yes" response and then insert one requiring a "no" response, hoping to catch the witness off-guard. This is called a "shotgun" approach. Listen to each question attentively and answer questions individually.

These are examples of questions that might arise while you are on the stand, followed by a suggested response:

— "Do you always call it abuse?" Answer: Child abuse medical centers see referred cases whereby someone already thinks that abuse has occurred, yet some percentage of the time it has not (akin to cardiovascular surgeons seeing a lot of heart disease). This is a function of how referrals are done, not a bias in diagnosis.

— "Do you testify only for the prosecution?" Answer: Your role is simply to provide the facts. However, when a situation is medically determined to not be abusive, there is usually no court proceeding.

— "Are you being paid?" Answer: You are being paid for your time, not opinion.

— "Do you back this reference?" Answer: No reference is absolutely authoritative. Avoid backing a specific reference because it implies your agreement with everything included in the reference.

— "Are your opinions based on speculation?" Answer: No, your opinion is based on reasonable medical certainty. Do not agree if the questioner implies that your opinions are based on speculation or guesswork.

— "Are there any differential diagnoses?" Answer: Physicians are trained to evaluate patients and assess the merits of differential diagnoses as well as the primary diagnosis. In the witness chair, the presentation of a differential diagnosis can imply doubt. If you are sure of the diagnosis offered and feel that there are no appropriate differential diagnoses, state that fact clearly and defend it on cross-examination.

— "Did you conduct a complete examination?" Answer: It would take hours to complete every possible maneuver that exists. Inevitably, there is an obscure examination detail you did not do. The answer is that you completed a *sufficient* examination to arrive at your diagnosis.

— "Did you consider a complete differential diagnosis?" Answer: Of course you did not document every conceivable, unlikely diagnosis, only those that were somewhat reasonable in the course of arriving at your final diagnosis.

— "Isn't child abuse a legal determination, not a medical one?" Answer: It is a medical diagnosis as well. The legal system and the medical system may not always agree.

— "Isn't anything possible?" Answer: No. While there may be a wide range of initial considerations, a good history and physical examination excludes thousands of diagnoses within minutes. Most diagnoses of abuse are not that difficult.

PROFILES AND LEVELS OF CERTAINTY

Profiling can lead to bias; therefore, it is important to understand what conclusions are appropriate or reasonable to draw. It is not scientifically or statistically appropriate to use a demographic profile of an individual to determine if that individual has committed abuse. Remember, individuals commit abuse, not groups. In contrast, it is reasonable to discuss the developmental capabilities of siblings in terms of their ability to have committed the abuse (eg, it takes an adult-sized person to shake a child). Special circumstances with adults may also arise (eg, a mother who has muscular dystrophy and cannot pick up a child).

Levels of certainty are legal concepts, and there is a purposeful vagueness to their definitions. Additionally, the translations to medical concepts are imprecise. As a rule:

— *Reasonable suspicion* (standard to make a report of child abuse) means that the claim is at least a significant possibility within the differential diagnosis; however, it might be more medically certain than that.

— *More likely than not* means that a judgment is more than 50% likely; this is probably the leading diagnostic possibility.

— *Clear and convincing* means somewhere between "more likely than not" and "beyond a reasonable doubt" and is the most likely medical possibility with a bit of complete uncertainty.

— *Beyond a reasonable doubt* means there is a reasonable degree of medical certainty. This is your diagnosis, and you would be willing to give medications or surgery based on this opinion. This does not mean a farfetched idea that cannot be conceived, and it does not mean metaphysical certainty, just reasonableness.

CROSS EXAMINATION

While the witness may feel unfairly attacked in court, it should not be seen as a personal attack. Of greater significance is the goal to convey the whole truth adequately and accurately to teach the judge and jury. In the process of court communication, several ploys might be used to discredit the witness or the testimony, so being aware of them is the best remedy to transcend their tactics and deliver the message. The following are the most common ploys:

— *Hostility:* This ploy is the most feared because it is meant to upset the witness and diminish the testimony. The goal is to get the witness to respond with anger or fear, which is inappropriate. Despite television and movie portrayals, the attorneys cannot randomly approach the witness. The opposing attorney and the judge are supposed to help protect the witness. The hostility may escalate gradually. If your pulse is racing and your voice rises, you are probably under hostile attack.

— The suggested solution when hostility is present is to be aware. Take a breath and change the paradigm. Slow down your answers slightly. Lean forward and look attentive. Drop the pitch of your voice a one-half note and get slightly quieter, though make sure you can still be heard by the jury. Be tolerant and sympathetic because judges and juries respond well to this. Realize that this attack will not last forever.

— *Nicety:* This ploy is sometimes referred to as the "Trojan horse" approach. Your competence will be amplified, and your opinion will be perceived as great. Nicety can be a dangerous tactic, as you might be set up to testify beyond your level of competence. Then, the lawyer will suddenly turn on you, or your testimony will be used against another, probably more competent, witness.

— The suggested solution is to be wary if it seems that you are being flattered. Be careful not to testify beyond your competence.

— ***Inconsistencies:*** With this ploy, if your opinion is not directly attacked, the issue of inconsistencies may arise. This is meant to impeach your testimony as lacking credibility.

— The suggested solution is to be aware of what was previously said and watch for slight differences in how a question is phrased because it may be the reason for a different sounding answer. For example: "The last time you asked a similar question, my answer was …. This question is slightly different, and my answer is…." If you are labelled as being inconsistent, dispute this and say why (unless you actually are inconsistent).

— ***Competency:*** Particularly for newer practitioners, this ploy can be upsetting. A lawyer may allege that you lack experience, are not certified in a variety of disciplines, did something incorrectly, or falsely asserted that people in your discipline do not know such answers.

— The suggested solution is to assert who you are (often through the other attorney) and be sure your CV is available. State that you were able to reach your opinions through accepted practices. Know that a jury is probably already impressed by your credentials and is most likely interested in what you have to say.

— ***Two-in-one:*** This ploy involves an attorney making a statement and then asking a question. The statement may be negative about you or your opinion. Sometimes there are 2 questions being asked. While the other attorney should object to a lawyer testifying, this does not happen every time.

— The suggested solution is to identify that there are 2 parts and address them individually. "For the first part of what you said my answer is…. For the second part, my answer is…." Do not allow incorrect characterization of your prior testimony. If this happens repetitively, the judge or an attorney will eventually intervene.

The goal of identifying and defusing these tactics is to maintain focus on the central facts of the case and the opinions of the expert witness.

SUMMARY

From the onset of the earliest medical encounter with a patient, medical professionals should anticipate some level of review for their decisions. This review can include a legal review in the context of a child abuse case. Preparation for review should encompass careful documentation of circumstances, clear delineation of who furnished what history, examination findings, and clear diagnoses. Preparation for legal review, however, also includes a review of records and a discussion with the attorney in advance. Once on the stand, be accurate in your answers – not minimizing or maximizing your opinion. Should various questioning tactics occur, try to relax, pay attention, and remain professional throughout. The expert's (your) role is to inform, not to win or lose a case.

DISCLAIMER

This author is considered an expert in his field as well an expert witness. He primarily constructed this chapter based on his comprehensive, cumulative knowledge and experience.

ADDITIONAL RESOURCES

1. Danner D. Do's and don'ts for experts. In: Shayne NT, ed. *Medical Evidence.* New York, NY: Practicing Law Institute; 1980:347-351.

2. Horsley JE, Carlova J. *Testifying in Court*. Oradell, NJ: Medical Economics Books; 1988.

3. The Ray E. Helfer Society. Guidelines for ethical testimony and court case review. The Ray E Helfer Society. https://www.helfersociety.org/ethical-testimony

4. Meltzer CC, Sze G, Rommelfanger KS, et al. Guidelines for the ethical use of neuroimages in medical testimony: report of a multidisciplinary consensus conference. *Am J Neuroradiol*. 2014;35(4):632-637.

Evidence-Based Treatment for Maltreated Children

Brian Allen, PsyD
Michelle P. Brown, PhD
Elizabeth Riden, LCSW
Chad E. Shenk, PhD

Objectives

After reviewing this chapter, the reader will be able to:

1. *Discuss the development of the mental health field, including the advent of evidence-based treatment (EBT).*

2. *Discuss common treatments, especially EBTs, for maltreated children.*

3. *Explain the mixed response to EBTs within the child mental health field.*

4. *Provide a detailed discussion of three EBTs, demonstrating the multifaceted nature of the emerging standard of care.*

What Is Evidence-based Mental Health Treatment?

The field of child mental health treatment is often baffling for providers in other disciplines. This confusion is largely a result of the rather unique historical development of the field and disparate ideas amongst clinicians about what treatment should entail. This chapter will trace the development of the field before discussing the advent of evidence-based treatment (EBT). Special attention will be given to understanding those treatment options typically available in the community for maltreated children, discussing why the move toward EBT within the child mental health field has been met with mixed responses from some providers, and providing 3 detailed examples of EBTs in order to demonstrate the multifaceted nature of the emerging standard of care.

Child Mental Health Treatment in Historical Context

Contemporary approaches to mental health treatment are generally considered to have originated with Sigmund Freud in his attempt to understand the development of anxiety and personality dysfunction within adult patients. As a result of his initial treatment cases, Freud developed the perspective that the root cause of mental illness among his female patients was a direct result of sexual abuse in childhood. He presented his idea to colleagues in Vienna shortly before the turn of the 20th century. The response was overwhelmingly critical, as Freud was essentially accusing affluent and esteemed men within a sexually inhibited society of molesting their daughters.[1] This presented Freud with a decision; either continue to promote his theory and almost assuredly face professional ruin or find a more acceptable way of explaining his clinical observations. He chose the latter. However, there was only 1 alternative explanation for the reports of sexual abuse discussed by his patients; if the molestation did not occur in reality, then the patients were unconsciously manufacturing these incidents. Consequently, Freud's emerging psychoanalytic theory would take as a foundational hypothesis, stating that children are driven by innate sexual motivations and prone to develop sexual fantasies of their parents.

According to Freud, children learn at a young age that sexual desires are not socially acceptable, especially those directed toward the parents, and as a result, the child's psyche develops defense mechanisms that either inhibit or manipulate the sexual fantasies into more tolerable forms. Nonetheless, the theory supposes that the true nature of these fantasies remain in the unconscious of the individual and may cause any number of psychiatric problems. Therefore, treatment prescribed by Freud emphasized bringing unconscious desires into one's conscious awareness where they could then be effectively addressed. To achieve such insight, Freud emphasized interpreting the content of dreams and free associations, believing he could identify important aspects of unconscious fantasies that slipped through the psyche's defenses.

Freud's daughter, Anna Freud, applied her father's technique to children, substituting play for free association and dream interpretation. She believed that analyzing the child's play could provide similar clues as to the unconscious feelings and thoughts of the child and subsequently bring them into the child's conscious awareness. In this model of treatment, the child is allowed to choose play materials and the clinician then attempts to interpret the likely symbolic meaning of the child's observable play. The hypothesis is that the child becoming aware of what the play represents in the unconscious, will help the child to more readily express their thoughts and feelings consciously, thus beginning the process of healing. In time, others would expand the techniques of the psychoanalytic play therapy approach. For instance, it is not uncommon to hear therapists suggest that children's drawings may convey unconscious content, such as the windows of a house darkened by curtains or blinds as suggestive that something traumatic occurred within the room. Perhaps the most popularized psychoanalytic technique with children is the sand tray. In this approach, a tray of sand is thought to represent the child's inner world and the child is encouraged to make a scene within the tray using a wide assortment of toys, figures, and other materials. The therapist then interprets the symbolism within the scene to assist the child in verbalizing unconscious thoughts.

After World War II, another approach to treatment emerged. Carl Rogers popularized the humanistic understanding of mental health as being largely a function of ***self-esteem***, which is defined as the degree to which one's perception of oneself deviates from the ideal self-image one has created. From this perspective, human motivation is oriented toward achieving one's ideal, and those who generally view themselves as closely approximating the ideal are considered to have high self-esteem, while those with a greater discrepancy between the 2 possess a lower self-esteem. Low self-esteem is considered to largely be the result of socially dictated constraints that inhibits one's efforts and is viewed as the root cause of problems as diverse as depression to aggression. Treatment for humanistic therapists is, consequently, focused on boosting one's self-esteem by encouraging self-acceptance, a sense of accomplishment, and personal value. For Rogers, the therapist is able to facilitate improved self-esteem and the alleviation of psychological distress through the provision of what he termed "necessary and sufficient conditions," which include unconditional positive regard for the patient, empathy, and genuineness.[2]

Likewise, humanistic clinicians believe low self-esteem underlies the development of mental health problems in children. Low self-esteem may be due to a caregiver who does not regularly provide self-affirming experiences or other events that similarly convey a message of inadequacy (eg, abuse, neglect). The therapist's focus then is to provide a safe environment wherein the child can express thoughts and feelings without judgment. This is usually performed in a play room with a wide assortment of toys and play materials available. The child is free to play however they choose, and the therapist then provides reflective and supportive comments, regardless of what is expressed by the child. Over time, the child begins to feel accepted and that their thoughts and feelings are valid, resulting, hypothetically, in an increase of self-esteem and a corresponding decrease in psychiatric problems. This humanistic approach to child treatment is often referred to as non-directive play therapy or child-centered play therapy in order to distinguish it from the psychoanalytic play therapy approaches discussed above. In practice, however, it is not uncommon to see child-centered and psychoanalytic play therapy approaches merged while treating a child.

Not long after Freud gained widespread notoriety for his ideas, a psychologist in the United States demonstrated how anxiety, specifically phobias, could be developed in a child through learning processes. In 1920, John B. Watson published a paper describing how he trained a young child, known in the literature as "Little Albert," to fear a white rat by pairing its presentation with a loud, frightening sound. A few years later, Mary Cover Jones demonstrated how the same learning processes could be used to treat a phobia. In her case, another young child, named "Little Peter," demonstrated a fear of rabbits. She simultaneously presented the boy with a rabbit and candy, providing a pleasant experience in the presence of the feared stimulus. She systematically decreased the distance between the boy and the rabbit to the point of the boy being able to hold and pet the rabbit without noticeable fear. These single cases were soon followed by other such demonstrations that experimented with different forms of delivery. Collectively, these cases suggested that the development of mental illness could be understood as the result of learning processes and that the same processes could be used to treat mental illness.

Much of the aforementioned work on learning approaches, or "behavioral" approaches as they are otherwise known, remained unfamiliar to the medical providers who were primarily responsible for mental health treatment prior to World War II. Watson and Cover Jones, as well as those that came immediately after them, were working in academia; Freud was a trained physician and his theory that emphasized innate drives fit better with the biological approach of medicine. After the war, mental health care systems in the United States and abroad were not sufficiently staffed to meet the needs of returning combat veterans and the war-exposed civilian populations. Psychologists, who historically focused on psychological testing, became more valued as treatment providers. Having been trained in academic programs focused on the science of psychology, many were familiar with the behavioral approaches pioneered by Watson and Cover Jones, and these ideas became more accepted in treatment settings. In addition, another branch of scientific learning theory was emerging that emphasized rewards and consequences for understanding the development and change of observed behavior. This field, known as operant conditioning and pioneered by B. F. Skinner, opened up new avenues of behavior modification that was directly applicable to the treatment of problematic child behavior.

By the 1970s, academic psychology was undergoing significant changes with the advent of the cognitive revolution. Scientific approaches to understanding behavior began to integrate findings from research on higher order processes such as memory, problem-solving, and decision-making. New approaches to treatment emphasized techniques that focused on evaluating the thoughts that people held about themselves, others, and the larger world. It was argued that changing the way people think could result in improvements of feelings and behaviors. Given its scientific underpinnings, this new cognitive therapy was quickly accepted within psychology and became integrated relatively easily and quickly with the prevailing behavioral methods (ie, cognitive-behavioral therapy [CBT]).

However, expanding the role of psychologists was not sufficient to meet the need for mental health services after the war, so clinicians trained to the Master's degree level in fields such as counseling and social work became more common as well. Many training programs, focused neither on academic psychology nor medicine, were often humanistic in orientation, resulting in a mental health marketplace where psychoanalytic, humanistic, and cognitive-behavioral approaches to treatment co-existed, often within the same agency or program. Today, it remains the case that the mental health field consists of a diversity of professional disciplines with different ideas and approaches to understanding both the etiology of mental illness and the most effective methods of treatment. It is commonplace for students to be taught various theoretical positions and instructed to identify the perspective that most suits their own disposition. As such, it is not unusual to hear a clinician describe oneself as a "child-centered play therapist" or a "cognitive-behavioral therapist."

UNDERSTANDING EVIDENCE-BASED TREATMENT

By the end of the 1970s, the scientific consensus was that psychotherapy yielded a greater chance of recovery from mental illness than if no such treatment was provided. However, the state of the science at the time was insufficient to demonstrate that one particular approach was superior to any other, offering the conclusion that all approaches were equally effective.[3] The prevailing assumption was that the common elements across models, primarily the provision of a therapeutic rapport, was principally responsible for the observed effect of treatment. Such an understanding was a boon to the humanistic and psychoanalytic approaches, as they emphasized rapport in their theories of change and they were less oriented toward the collection of scientific data than the cognitive and behavioral fields.

By the dawn of the 1980s, however, research methodology had progressed and well-controlled randomized clinical trials (RCTs) were increasingly common in the literature. The results of such RCTs were clearly demonstrating that some treatment approaches yielded greater benefit than others for the treatment of specific conditions. As the data continued to accumulate throughout the 1980s and 1990s, the majority of studies supported interventions originating from the behavioral and cognitive traditions. This was partly due to empirical investigation already being a foundational hallmark of these approaches to understanding behavior. Clinicians from psychoanalytic and humanistic persuasions argued that their approaches were not as amenable to examination through RCT methodology, given their emphasis on the curative effect of the therapeutic rapport and the importance of clinical judgement. It was a contentious debate that remains to this day: is the therapeutic endeavor one of science that should be informed by the results of rigorous RCTs (favored by cognitive and behavioral proponents) or one focused on the clinician's artful delivery of therapeutic rapport and informed by that clinician's intuition and experience (favored by humanistic and psychoanalytic proponents)?

Given that practically all therapeutic approaches incorporate an effective therapeutic rapport as the foundation for treatment delivery, the scientific focus shifted to identifying those techniques that can yield outcomes greater than therapeutic rapport alone. Many of these efforts utilized child-centered play therapy as the control condition in RCTs (or the comparable humanistic approach with teenage patients), and positive results for the experimental interventions suggested their superiority over a treatment focused solely on therapeutic rapport. In a contemporary scientific sense, these interventions are regarded as "evidence-based treatments (EBTs)." The majority of EBTs are derived from the cognitive and behavioral fields. Although EBTs originating in the humanistic (eg, motivational interviewing) and psychoanalytic perspectives (eg, interpersonal therapy) are available, they are less commonly implemented with youth. It is commonly regarded that the combination of clinical skill and scientifically supported techniques provides the optimum approach to treatment. State and federal agencies, as well as non-profit organizations such as the National Children's Alliance, have made concerted efforts to direct funding and training efforts toward EBTs.

Proponents of treatment approaches not generally considered EBTs argue that the designation is too restrictive, funding is too difficult to obtain, and that theoretical bias against their particular approach is rampant. In addition to emphasizing the centrality of therapeutic rapport, many of these proponents argue that their approaches do possess convincing empirical evidence. For instance, they often point to RCTs suggesting their preferred intervention performs better than a waitlist where participants received no treatment or to a meta-analysis of non-controlled studies that demonstrate the quantity of studies with positive results. Based on these results, it is not uncommon for proponents to suggest that these interventions are "evidence-based," as they believe the evidence clearly supports the validity of their approach. At other times, the focus of the argument may emphasize the importance of clinical judgment with case studies presented as evidence. A more recent argument is that certain treatment approaches may be capable of ameliorating neurological and physiological changes caused by childhood abuse and trauma. Although it is an interesting hypothetical proposition, there is currently no compelling replicated evidence that any psychotherapeutic treatment induces such neurobiological improvements among children.

Unfortunately, the majority of clinical training programs continue to emphasize theoretical perspective over scientific evidence. Training is rarely available in any particular EBT during the course of one's graduate studies, which then results in most graduating clinicians attempting to apply a broad theoretical approach of their own choosing to a multitude of presenting concerns in practice. Training in an EBT often necessitates practicing clinicians to expend time and financial resources to attend intensive trainings. Even if a clinician desires to practice using EBTs, noted problems with dissemination can make it difficult to know which interventions possess sufficient empirical support, and locating an accessible training in that approach is difficult as well. Additionally, there is yet another problem to offering children state-of-the-science interventions. Contrary to what many clinicians are taught to believe, no single intervention is a panacea capable of treating the multitude of presenting concerns that may arise following childhood maltreatment. If a single agency wishes to provide a complete service array for maltreated children, having multiple interventions available onsite is necessary, and each intervention requires its own specialized training. To highlight this point, 3 well-known EBTs for use with maltreated children and youth are discussed below.

TRAUMA-FOCUSED COGNITIVE BEHAVIORAL THERAPY

Trauma-focused cognitive behavioral therapy (TF-CBT) was originally developed to reduce posttraumatic stress symptoms in children and adolescents, aged 3 to 17 years, who had experienced sexual abuse.[4] Following 25 years of RCT research, multiple systematic reviews agree that TF-CBT is the most well-established, evidence-based treatment for reducing posttraumatic stress symptoms and other mental health sequelae (eg, depression, anxiety, and behavioral problems) in children who have experienced various types of trauma, including child maltreatment.[5] Furthermore, RCTs have shown that TF-CBT is more effective in reducing these symptoms than treatment focused on the development of rapport (eg, non-directive play therapy). The intervention is a structured, components-based protocol broken up into 3 different treatment phases that span 8-25 sessions (**Table 6-1**).

Table 6-1. Examples of Cognitive Behavioral Treatment Techniques	
TECHNIQUE	RECOMMENDATION
Exposure	Akin to systematic desensitization, exposure involves gradual experiencing of thoughts and feelings related to abuse to reduce painful symptoms elicited by cues and reminders.
Psychoeducation	Clinicians offer and discuss realistic information related to experiences of and reactions to abuse to counteract misassumptions and negative attributions.
Emotional identification and regulation	Children are taught to recognize and link physical sensations with underlying feelings and thoughts. Through techniques such as relaxation or cognitive restructuring, they learn to modulate negative, distressing emotions.
Behavior management	Often used with parents, behavior management focuses on teaching and practicing contingency management and counter-conditioning strategies to improve the parent-child relationship, decrease externalizing behavior, and replace coercive and punitive discipline with positive methods.
Cognitive restructuring	Children and parents are taught to recognize and correct underlying, maladaptive thoughts, and assumptions that give rise to emotional, physical, and behavioral symptoms.
Social skills and problem solving	By learning to recognize social cues, resolve conflicts, and interact in socially desirable ways, children reduce social isolation and improve positive, supportive relationships.

Key aspects of the treatment protocol include the following:

— Three phases, which are approximately equal in length:

— (1) **Skill development**, which focuses on the development of effective coping skills through psychoeducation, instruction in parenting skills, and training in various forms of relaxation and emotion regulation techniques

— (2) **Trauma narration and processing**, where the child develops a factual account of their trauma experiences and re-evaluates maladaptive thoughts related to the experience

— (3) **Real world mastery,** which focuses on demonstrating successful application of learned skills to various settings through exercises such as sharing the narrative with a caregiver who is prepared to offer a supportive, compassionate response, confronting feared stimuli associated with the trauma, and learning skills to enhance future safety.

— Engaging the youth in **gradual exposure**, which is defined as encouraging the child, in carefully calibrated increments, to talk and write about increasingly upsetting aspects of the trauma with each step being slightly more difficult than the previous step. This is done in order to desensitize the child to reminders, memories, and physical stimuli associated with abusive experiences. This experience culminates in the construction of the trauma narrative, which represents a focused dose of exposure, considered the primary agent of change in TF-CBT.

— Actively involving caregivers throughout TF-CBT treatment. Beyond learning parenting skills, parents also receive psychoeducation about trauma, are taught the same coping skills that children are learning, and are asked to practice the skills with their children and encourage their effective use. The therapist also reads newly developed portions of the trauma narrative to the caregiver throughout the sessions and allows the caregiver to process their own thoughts and feelings related to the child's experience. In the third phase of treatment, the child reads the completed narrative to the caregiver to provide the child an experience of successfully sharing the details of their abuse with a supportive adult in his or her life. Prior to this conjoint session, the therapist meets with the caregiver to ensure they will be able to provide an appropriate and supportive response when the child reads the narrative.

PARENT-CHILD INTERACTION THERAPY

Parent-child interactive therapy (PCIT) is a parent-training intervention that was originally developed in the early 1970s.[6] Over the past 40 years, through rigorous clinical trial research, PCIT has become regarded as the best-practice model for the treatment of behavioral problems in children (eg, defiance, frequent temper tantrums, aggression). PCIT is an intervention for children ages 2.5 to 7 years and works with parents and children together to improve the quality of the parent-child relationship and to shape more desired behavior from the child by teaching the parent a specific set of skills. Parents gain confidence in their ability to manage their children's behaviors, resulting in reduced stress and physical forms of discipline, and consequently, lower rates of recidivism with the child welfare system when compared to services-as-usual.[7]

PCIT is unique among child treatment programs in that it focuses on changing the behaviors of both the child and the parent using a live coaching format. Most often, a trained therapist coaches from behind a one-way mirror, using a "bug-in-the-ear" device to communicate with the parent. In this way, the parent receives live, in-the-moment coaching from the clinician in the implementation of the parenting skills being taught. PCIT is a manualized, 12-14 session treatment protocol using 2 phases of administration: child directed interaction (CDI) and parent directed interaction (PDI). The 2 phases are described below:

1. *CDI:* The goal of this phase is to enhance the parent-child relationship and teach the use of positive attention to increase desired behaviors. Parents are taught a set of "avoid" skills, including limiting the number of questions and commands used in conversation and eliminating words the child will perceive as negative or critical, such as "no," "don't," "stop," and "quit." Parents are also taught to praise desired behavior, as well as provide other forms of attention, such as reflecting the child's verbalizations and describing the child's play (**Table 6-2**). In addition, parents are taught to ignore minor misbehavior and negative attention-seeking behaviors (ie, selective attention). Parents use these skills during a structured, child-led play time in weekly therapy sessions and at home on a daily basis. With practice and daily use, the skills begin to generalize to other daily activities outside of play time.

2. *PDI:* The goals of this phase are to help parents gain control over their child's behavior while simultaneously teaching the child to listen and follow directions and rules. During PDI, parents are instructed to continue using CDI skills in order to maintain and continue building a strong parent-child relationship while also learning the importance of consistency, predictability, and follow-through with consequences for non-compliance and rule-breaking behavior. The clinician teaches and coaches the parent in how to deliver effective and direct commands. Direct commands are specific, age appropriate, positively stated, and given in a neutral tone of voice. Parents are also taught how to implement an effective time-out procedure.

PCIT treatment is concluded when parents meet pre-defined mastery criteria in both CDI and PDI skills, and the child's behavior has improved.

Table 6-2. Examples of "Do" and "Don't" Behaviors for Parents

Dos	Reasons	Examples
Praise: Labeled praise tells your child exactly what you like.	— Increases the behavior that is praised — Shows approval — Improves child's self-esteem — Makes child feel good	— "Good job with that tower." — "You drew a pretty tree." — "Nice drawing." — "Thank you for sharing." — "I like how gently you're putting the crayons away."
Enjoy: Enjoyment means that you act happy and warm when you play with your child.	— Lets your child know that you are enjoying the time you are spending together — Adds to the warmth of the play — Increases closeness between you and your child	— Child: (carefully placing a blue Lego on a tower) — Parents: (gently touching the child's back) "You are *really* being gentle with the toys."

Don'ts	Reasons	Examples
Commands: Commands tell your child to do something.	— Takes the lead away from the child — Can cause conflict	**Indirect commands:** — "Let's play with the farm next." — "Can you tell me what animal this is?" **Direct commands:** — "Give me the pigs." — "Please sit down next to me." — "Look at this."
Stop Aggressive Behavior: Stop play for aggressive and destructive behavior.	— Aggressive and destructive behaviors cannot be ignored because they can be dangerous.	— Child: (hits parent) — Parent: (gathering toys) "Special time is over because you hit me." — Child: "Oh, oh, oh, Mom. I'm sorry. Please, I'll be good." — Parent: "Special time is over today. We will play again tomorrow."

DIALECTICAL BEHAVIOR THERAPY FOR ADOLESCENTS

Dialectical behavior therapy (DBT) was originally developed as a behavioral treatment for chronically suicidal adults who were diagnosed with borderline personality disorder, many of whom have a history of child maltreatment. After several decades of RCT research, DBT is now regarded as a well-established intervention for the treatment of suicidal risk and behavior. Dialectical behavior therapy for adolescents (DBT-A) is an adaptation of DBT, appropriate for those aged 12 to 18 years with presenting concerns related to suicidal ideation, suicide attempts, non-suicidal self-injury, or chronic emotion dysregulation, including those with a history of child maltreatment.[8] Randomized controlled trials evaluating the effectiveness of DBT-A have shown its superiority in reducing suicidal risk and behavior when compared to alternative treatments. These trials have demonstrated the effectiveness of DBT-A across acute in-patient, partial hospitalization, and traditional outpatient settings. DBT-A is a manualized, 19 to 24-week treatment protocol using 4 modes of administration:

1. Adolescents meet weekly for individual therapy with a DBT-A trained provider. Individual therapy focuses on the assessment of suicidal risk and behavior through of the repeated chaining and sequencing of both public and private events, such as changes in affect, cognition, and behavior that reliably leads to increases in suicidal ideation, non-suicidal self-injury, and suicidal behavior. Individual therapy also provides treatment planning opportunities where structured application and generalization of newly acquired DBT-A skills allows for the prevention of suicidal risk and behavior by targeting the events that reliably occur earlier in the sequence to suicidal behavior.

2. Both adolescents and their caregivers participate in group skills training. Adolescents learn 4 types of skills that are designed to prevent suicidal risk and behavior: 1) distress tolerance skills to reduce subjective distress in a crisis, 2) emotion regulation skills to promote overall mood and reduce negative affect, 3) interpersonal effectiveness skills for initiating and maintaining relationships, and 4) mindfulness skills for promoting awareness of suicidal risk and the need to use DBT-A skills. Caregivers also learn a variety of skills, including traditional behavioral parent training for reducing non-compliance as well as validation, which teaches parents to accept and understand an adolescent's thoughts and emotions in real-time to promote overall emotion regulation.

3. Both adolescents and caregivers are provided telephone consultation with a DBT-A provider between individual therapy sessions to promote skill acquisition and generalization.

4. All DBT-A providers participate in clinical supervision teams that provide expert feedback on treatment planning and reduce provider burnout.

SUMMARY

The field of mental health treatment has evolved considerably over the past century, including the subfield of child treatment. This chapter has clearly defined treatment protocols for a wide range of presenting concerns, including sequelae commonly experienced following child abuse and neglect. The field continues to grapple, however, with making these interventions more readily accessible to patients and with how to improve clinician implementation and fidelity to evidence-based treatment protocols. Even as these dissemination issues are being addressed, research is emerging that suggests specific identifiable components of EBTs (eg, exposure, parent training) may be driving clinical outcome, and it is unclear whether the future of the field will continue to promote the delivery of a branded treatment protocol or emphasize the implementation of the most effective individual components. The child mental health field, like most fields, is in a constant state of evolution and discovery in order to benefit maltreated children in need.

REFERENCES

1. Masson JM. *The Assault on Truth: Freud's Suppression of the Seduction Theory.* Farrar, Straus, and Giroux; 1984.

2. Rogers CR. The necessary and sufficient conditions of therapeutic personality change. *J Consult Psych.* 1957;21:95-103.

3. Smith ML, Glass GV. Meta-analysis of psychotherapy outcome studies. *Amer Psych.* 1977;32:752-760.

4. Cohen JA, Mannarino AP, Deblinger E. *Treating Trauma and Traumatic Grief in Children and Adolescents.* 2nd ed. Guilford Press; 2017.

5. Dorsey S, McLaughlin KA, Kerns SEU, et al. Evidence base update for psychosocial treatments for children and adolescents exposed to traumatic events. *J Clin Child Adol Psych.* 2017;46:303-330.

6. McNeil CB, Hembree-Kigin TL. *Parent-Child Interaction Therapy.* 2nd ed. Springer; 2010.

7. Chaffin M, Silovsky JF, Funderburk B, et al. Parent-child interaction therapy with physically abusive parents: efficacy for reducing future abuse reports. *J Consult Clin Psych.* 2004;72:500-510.

8. Miller AL, Rathus JH, Linehan MM. *Dialectical Behavior Therapy with Suicidal Adolescents.* Guilford Press; 2007.

Chapter 7

PREVENTING CHILD MALTREATMENT

Vincent J. Palusci, MD, MS, FAAP

OBJECTIVES

After reviewing this chapter, the reader will be able to:

1. *Describe what prevention is and who implements it.*

2. *Explain the levels of prevention and how they apply to populations.*

3. *Outline elements of successful prevention programs.*

4. *Identify and describe specific prevention programs.*

DEFINING PREVENTION

The term **prevention** refers to the methods by which there is an attempt to lower the rates of child maltreatment (ie, abuse of any kind, including physical or sexual abuse, and neglect). There are various ideas about what prevention actually means and which strategies are considered effective. The 3 levels of prevention were first described in the 1950s and later refined by Gordon[1] in 1983, distinguishing between strategies for different populations and setting the foundation for prevention efforts. Those levels are:

— **Primary/Universal:** Prevention efforts aimed at the general population for the purpose of keeping maltreatment from happening

— **Secondary/Selective:** Prevention efforts aimed at a particular group with increased risk in an effort to prevent maltreatment from happening

— **Tertiary/Indicated:** Prevention efforts aimed at inhibiting the further maltreatment of those who have already been victimized, including treatment to reduce harm from the maltreatment

The Centers for Disease Control and Prevention (CDC)[2] has emphasized that maltreatment operates within a societal context and responds to a spectrum of prevention strategies over time. The CDC proposes thinking of these strategies in terms of *when* the prevention occurs (ie, before or after), *who* the focus is (ie, everyone, those at greatest risk, those *who* have already experienced it), and at *what* point to intervene (ie, individual, relationship, community, or society level). These strategies emphasize a shift away from risk reduction, the previously predominant approach that focused on individual targets of maltreatment, to one that considers environmental and societal factors, as well as positive social change. There are also definitions of prevention based on when action should be taken. These definitions apply to all populations:

— **Primary:** Taking action *before* child maltreatment has occurred to prevent it from happening

— **Secondary:** Intervening *right after* child maltreatment has occurred

— **Tertiary:** Working *over a period of time* to change conditions in the environments that promote or support child maltreatment

IMPLEMENTING PREVENTION

The prevention of child maltreatment begins with a caregivers having access to the necessary resources for successful child-raising; therefore, families are the key to prevention efforts. Early intervention is more effective in preventing abuse and neglect, spends less community funding (eg, judicial costs), and improves individuals' overall health and well-being.

Maltreatment prevention should begin with national leaders taking action to better support the family unit. The US Advisory Board on Child Abuse and Neglect[3] reported that child maltreatment is an emergency that requires leadership through professional societies and research. Prevention, however, is not explicitly the responsibility of any 1 agency, profession, or program, but is rather best framed as a multidisciplinary responsibility to create a society that is less conducive to child maltreatment. In this paradigm, individual skill development, community and provider education, coalition building, organizational change, and policy innovations are all part of the prevention solution. Professionals who provide clinical or supportive services to victims of maltreatment and their families are providing tertiary prevention. These professionals are obligated to remain aware of and support other community prevention efforts, as well as refer victims and their families to the appropriate resources.

Child maltreatment is a product of various conditions and risk factors within the family and society as a whole. To lower the risk of child maltreatment, families should have their basic needs fulfilled (eg, adequate food, clothing, shelter, affordable income, child care, and education). While many of these foundations are the responsibility of society and government, society cannot assume that child maltreatment prevention is a function of government alone. Government leaders must represent both the public and the private sectors. The private sector (eg, companies) must support families by offering intervention and prevention programs in the workplace as well as encouraging and funding community-wide efforts on behalf of all children.

PREVENTION STRATEGIES

There is increasing evidence demonstrating the elements of successful interventions, the most beneficial populations and programs, and the best implementation research shows which goals have been met. It is important to note, however, that some forms of maltreatment (eg, neglect and sexual abuse) are different than other forms of maltreatment (eg, physical abuse) and may need different prevention strategies. The American Academy of Pediatrics has made prevention recommendations specifically for pediatricians.[4]

Daro[5] provided 3 important goals of prevention efforts:

1. Reduce the incidence of maltreatment and neglect.

2. Minimize the chance that children who are maltreated will be revictimized.

3. Break the cycle of maltreatment by providing victims with the support and resources needed to better parent in the next generation.

Systematic comparative prevention effectiveness research is in its early infancy, and the long-term success of most programs is still being researched.[6] Most strategies, such as home visiting, are not uniformly effective in reducing all forms of maltreatment, but they do appear to improve parenting or 1 or more risk factors, especially in "high-risk" families. Additional health and well-being outcomes, such as improved physical growth and development for infants, have also been noted in the research, although sometimes without concurrent measurable reductions in child maltreatment.

Many available intervention strategies, which vary by method and approach, tailor their programs to 1 or more levels of prevention, and are aimed at addressing different risk factors in different populations (**Table 7-1**). These strategies may focus on children, caregivers, caregiver-child dyads, or the environment in which caregivers raise children. These strategies are appropriate given our understanding that child maltreatment occurs as a result of various factors that simultaneously act on the caregivers, children, families/relationships, communities, and levels of society.[7]

Table 7-1. Examples of Prevention Strategies		
LEVEL	STRATEGY	EXAMPLE(S)
Primary	Prepregnancy/ Perinatal care	**"Safe haven" laws.** Allows the caregiver, or an agent of the caregiver, to remain anonymous and shielded from prosecution for abandonment or neglect in exchange for surrendering the baby at a "safe haven" (eg, hospital, police station, fire department). All 50 states, the District of Columbia, and Puerto Rico have enacted "safe haven" legislation. After implimenting these laws, there was a 66.7% drop in infant homicide.[8]
	Newborn abusive head trauma education	**Dias.** A program that educates new caregivers on the dangers of infant shaking and teaches the proper methods to use when infants cry.[9] **Period of PURPLE Crying.** Uses a brief video and written material to educate new caregivers about normal crying and how to cope with infant crying.[10]
	Home visiting	**Nurse Family Partnership, Healthy Families America.** Sends nurses or paraprofessionals to the homes of all new babies and young children in order to provide information and support for the caregivers.[11-17]
	Reducing physical discipline	**No Hit Zones.** Reduces the use of corporal punishment and physical discipline, calling for health institutions and communities to proclaim that "No parent shall hit a child, no parent shall hit a parent, and no child shall hit a parent, and no child shall hit another child."[18]
	Sexual abuse prevention	**School sexual abuse education.** Provides information to school age children about "good touch/bad touch," appropriate contact, permission to tell, and communicates that the child is not responsible for their sexual abuse. **Organizational policies.** Various local and national policies for youth-serving organizations that provide increased education and supervision during activities with children.[19]
	Social capital building	**Triple P Parenting Program.** Program with 5 intervention levels of increasing intensity and narrowing population reach. Combines various targeted interventions to ensure a safe environment (eg, promoting learning, using assertive discipline, maintaining reasonable expectations, and taking care of oneself as a caregiver), which then translates into 35 specific caregiver skills and strategies.[20,21] **Prevention Zones.** Incorporates prevention into all levels of community services and changes the discussion from penalizing and criminalizing to promoting and supporting successful caregiving.[22]

(continued)

Level	Strategy	Example(s)
Secondary	Family wellness	**Parenting programs.** These include trainings, classes, family preservation programs, and empowerment/strengths-based approaches.[23,24]
	Caregiver training	**Family Nurturing Program.** Specific program that teaches caregivers empathy, decreased corporal punishment, and other techniques.[24]
	Medical services	**Safe Environment for Every Child (SEEK) program.** Uses a social worker in addition to pediatric providers to screen for and repsond to risk factors.[25] Families using SEEK had fewer reports of child maltreatment to child protective services (CPS), fewer incidents of medical non-adherence and delayed immunizations, and less harsh punishment by caregivers when compared to a control group.[26]
	Adolescent services	**Teen mothers groups.** Provides medical services for both baby and mother during the infant's first year of life, improving immunization rates and child development.[27]
Tertiary	Mandated reporting	**Counseling after psychologic maltreatment.** Decreases recurrence.[28,29] **Therapy groups for children exposed to violence.** Special groups for children exposed to violence that have a goal of improving behavior and reduce trauma symptoms.[30]
	Fatality review	**Child fatality review programs.** Designs strategies to prevent future deaths.[31]

Table 7-1. Examples of Prevention Strategies *(continued)*

ELEMENTS OF SUCCESSFUL PROGRAMS

To shape strategies of successful prevention programs, evidence-based standards should be used, but there remains room for creativity and the use of feedback from diverse community settings in order to meet their unique needs and situations. Many program leaders have noted that a lack of funds has hampered their ability to be truly comprehensive, to reach broader audiences, and to use creative strategies. Therefore, demands for quality prevention programs need to be combined with demands for adequate funding so that these programs can be made accessible to the entire community.

The US Children's Bureau[32] has suggested that all prevention programs need to commit to a set of practice principles that have been found effective across diverse disciplines and programs. The Bureau has published a list of "best-practice" standards that are representative of elements at the core of effective intervention strategies. Service providers and policy advocates should support strategies that embrace the following principles:

— A strong theory for change that identifies core outcomes and clear pathways for addressing them, including specific strategies and curriculum content

— A recommended duration, dosage, and clear guidelines for all those enrolled in programs, specifically for determining when to discontinue or extend services

— A clear, well-defined target population with identified eligibility criteria and strategy for reaching and engaging with them

— A strategy for guiding program staff through balancing the delivery of program content with a family's cultural beliefs and immediate circumstances

— A method for training program staff on how to best deliver the program model under a supervisory system, supporting direct service staff and guiding their ongoing practice

— Reasonable number of maintained caseloads so that program staff can accomplish core program objectives

— The systematic collection of information on participant and staff characteristics and experiences to ensure that the services are being implemented with fidelity to the model, intent, and structure

PROGRAMS AND SERVICES FOR NEW CAREGIVERS

To prevent child maltreatment, it is necessary that a wide range of training, services, resources, and policies be available to caregivers. In addition, all programs should be culturally sensitive and targeted to the appropriate developmental level of the caregivers. Helfer[33] noted a "window of opportunity" during the perinatal period for enhancing caregiver-child interactions and preventing physical abuse. This period, defined as 1 year before birth to 18 to 24 months of life, is a critical time to teach new caregivers the skills for interacting with their newborns. Several program models have shown promise based on key periods within this time frame, including prepregnancy planning, early conception, late pregnancy, prelabor and labor, immediately after delivery, and at home with the child. Opportunities for prevention in the early months of life include teaching parents and caregivers how to cope with infant crying and providing a safe sleep environment for their infant.

New caregivers benefit from specialized instruction and support services. Programs for new caregivers should include the following:

— Acknowledging how tough caregiving can be (our culture tends to simply congratulate new caregivers)

— Screening for postpartum depression

— Specialized caregiver support, both formal and informal

— Increasing the caregiver's knowledge of child development, child and home management, and the demands involved in child-raising

— Enhancing the caregiver's skill for coping with the stresses of infant and child care (eg, how to respond to an infant's cries), especially in children with special needs

— Enhancing caregiver-child bonding and communication skills

— Increasing access to child care, as well as social and health services for all family members

FAMILY WELLNESS AND PARENTING PROGRAMS

Family wellness programs include a variety of caregiver and family interventions that have demonstrated several positive outcomes. Assessment for these family programs can be problematic due to research on them often being grouped together, but meta-analyses do show promising reductions in child maltreatment.[34] These family wellness programs range from short-term counseling to parenting classes and sometimes include home visiting services for families that are "at-risk" for maltreatment. Research shows that "at-risk" families who do not receive proper education on child care have higher rates of child maltreatment (and hospitalizations as a result), along with more caregiver arrests.[35] Intensive family preservation programs that have high levels of participant involvement, social support, and an empowerment/ strengths-based approach, prove to be more effective than others. Strengths-based practice involves a shift from a deficit-based approach, which emphasizes problems and pathology, to a family-based approach, which acknowledges each child's and family's unique strengths and challenges and uses the family as a partner to develop and implement the program plan.

Caregiver programs often involve training that includes reviewing child development, teaching and practicing specific skills, identifying and addressing maladaptive behaviors, and helping caregivers manage their own emotions and respond to stress. In order to maximize positive outcomes, these programs should address the following as well[36]:

— Appropriate length, delivery mode, and program setting for each unique family

— Relationship with the trainer

— Family socioeconomic status

— Inclusion of fathers

— Need for additional child therapy

— Home visiting

Research on caregiver programs is moderate due to the range of programs and the variables that exist therein. However, a CDC meta-analysis of caregiver training programs looked at program components and delivery methods that ultimately had the greatest effect on child behavior and caregiver skills.[23] This study concluded that teaching caregivers emotional communication skills and positive child interaction skills (eg, correct use of time out, consistent responses), while requiring practice with their children each session, was the most effective method for acquiring successful parenting skills and behaviors, and led to a decrease in children's externalizing behaviors. Palusci et al.[24] in their study of the Family Nurturing Program that utilized these techniques found that parents with a variety of problems (eg, incarceration, substance abuse, stress), had improved empathy, understanding of child development, and other improved caregiving skills after an 8-week program of interactive classes.

HOME VISITING

Home visiting programs aim to prevent child maltreatment by influencing caregiver factors that are linked to maltreatment.[36] These factors are:

— Inadequate knowledge of child development

— Belief in the use of harsh parenting practices

— Lack of empathy

— Insensitive, unresponsive parenting

— Stress and lack of social support

— The inability to provide a safe and stimulating home environment

By changing these factors, home visiting programs promote children's health (eg, enhanced immunization), development (eg, earlier identification of and treatment for delays), wellbeing, and safety. In addition to preventing maltreatment, some studies even show a 40% reduction rate of maltreatment cases.[11,12]

Home visiting, in programs such as the Nurse-Family Partnership and Healthy Families America, has also been shown to[13,15-17,37]:

— Consistently reduce preterm and low-weight births

— Increase the amount of well-child or well-baby care medical visits

— Reduce deaths and hospitalizations for child injuries and ingestions

— Increase time between pregnancies

— Increase overall family satisfaction

— Save taxpayers money

PROGRAMS TO PREVENT NEGLECT AND SEXUAL ABUSE

Although different in manifestation, all forms of child maltreatment share common causes. However, special attention should be granted to neglect and sexual abuse prevention as the causes of these types of maltreatment differ from other forms.

As stated earlier, caregivers require basic resources in order to provide proper care for their children. To prevent child neglect, the following basics are needed for free or "for cost," and they should be based on the caregiver's ability to pay, along sliding scales, or under provisions of employee insurance or assistance programs[38,39]:

— Accessible and developmentally appropriate child care to be made a national priority

— Decent and affordable housing

— Adequate mental health, medical and dental care, and nutritious food

— Culturally sensitive programs that address jobs, substance abuse prevention and treatment, and family support in order to break a cycle of poverty and chronic violence

— Ability to function at adequate levels so they can focus on their children's needs

Although some cases of child sexual abuse are immediately apparent, the vast majority of cases are discovered through a child's own accidental or purposeful disclosure of abuse. Children often grapple with whether to tell, who to tell, and when to disclose so as to minimize negative outcomes to themselves or their families. In addition, these children may be faced with adults who are unprepared to respond appropriately because of their own lack of information, fears, or emotional responses.[40] Therefore, the major responsibility for prevention is placed on the child victims themselves, something not seen in other forms of maltreatment.[41]

In an effort to address child sexual abuse at the source, the CDC[19] also developed a comprehensive strategy for preventing adults from becoming offenders. These methods include:

— Educating adolescents and young children on healthy sexuality during the preteen and teenage years

— Training professionals and volunteers who work with children, on identifying and helping children who are being abused and teaching those children to protect themselves and detect potential molesters

— Educating new parents on early attachment and bonding with their first babies, including information on appropriate touch and how to recognize signs of sexual abuse in children

— Making institutional changes that ensure that all child-serving organizations screen (eg, run background checks on), train, and monitor volunteers and staff

COMMUNITY STRATEGIES

Community strategies to prevent child abuse and promote child protection have focused on creating supportive residential communities where residents share a belief in collective responsibility to protect children from harm while expanding the range of services and instrumental supports directly available to parents.[22] When focusing on community building, programs can mobilize volunteers and engage diverse sectors within the community (eg, first responders, the faith community, local businesses, and civic groups) in working to prevent child abuse. This mobilization can exert synergistic impact on other desired community outcomes, such as economic development and better health care.

SUMMARY

There are a variety of prevention strategies and programs with varying evidence for the reduction of child maltreatment. These strategies vary depending on the population they aim to serve, but they all share the common goal of reducing the rate of child maltreatment through child and family support, education, and training. The multidisciplinary approach of involving children, caregivers, medical professionals, social workers, and the community at large ensures that the safety and well-being of children is a priority. While all potential strategies for preventing child maltreatment could not be covered in this chapter, professionals and communities can confidently support strategies such as home visits, referrals for parent education and treatment, and improved funding and access to other evidence-based efforts in their community.

REFERENCES

1. Gordon RS. An operational classification of disease prevention. *Public Health Rep.* 1983;98(2):107-109.

2. Fortson BL, Klevens J, Merrick MT, Gilbert LK, Alexander SP. *Preventing Child Abuse and Neglect: A Technical Package for Policy, Norm, and Programmatic Activities.* National Center for Injury Prevention and Control, Centers for Disease Control and Prevention; 2016.

3. US Advisory Board on Child Abuse and Neglect. *Child Abuse and Neglect: Critical First Steps in Response to a National Emergency.* Health and Human Services; 1990.

4. Flaherty EG, Stirling J; American Academy of Pediatrics Committee on Child Abuse and Neglect. Clinical report: the pediatrician's role in child maltreatment prevention. *Pediatrics.* 2010;126(4);833-841.

5. Daro D, Dodge DA. Creating community responsibility for child protection: possibilities and challenges. *Future Child.* 2009;19(2):67-93.

6. MacMillan HL, Wathen CN, Barlow J, Fergusson DM, Leventhal JM, Taussig HN. Interventions to prevent child maltreatment and associated impairment. *Lancet.* 2009;373(9659):250-266.

7. World Health Organization, International Society for the Prevention of Child Abuse and Neglect. *Preventing Child Maltreatment: A Guide to Taking Action and Generating Evidence.* Geneva, Switzerland: World Health Organization; 2006.

8. Wilson RF, Klevens J, Williams D, Xu L. Infant homicide within the context of safe haven laws—United States, 2008-2017. *MMWR Morb Mortal Wkly Rep.* 2020;69(39):1385-1390.

9. Dias MS, Smith K, DeGuehery K, Mazur P, Li V, Shaffer ML. Preventing abusive head trauma among infant and young children: a hospital-based, parent education program. *Pediatrics.* 2005;115(4):e470-e477.

10. Barr RG, Rivara FP, Barr M, et al. Effectiveness of educational materials designed to change knowledge and behaviors regarding crying and shaken-baby syndrome in mothers of newborns: a randomized, controlled trial. *Pediatrics.* 2009;123(3):972-980.

11. Sweet MA, Appelbaum MI. Is home visiting an effective strategy? A meta-analytic review of home visiting programs for families with young children. *Child Dev.* 2004;75(5):1435-1456.

12. Olds DL. The nurse-family partnership: an evidence-based preventative intervention. *Infant Ment Health J.* 2006;27(1):5-25.

13. Kitzman H, Olds DL, Knudtson MD, et al. Prenatal and infancy nurse home visiting and 18-year outcomes of a randomized trial. *Pediatrics.* 2019; 144(6):e20183876.

14. Gomby DS. The promise and limitations of home visiting: implementing effective programs. *Child Abuse Negl.* 2007;31(8):793-799.

15. DuMont K, Mitchell-Herzfeld S, Greene R, et al. Healthy Families New York (HFNY) randomized trial: effects on early child abuse and neglect. *Child Abuse Negl.* 2008;32(2):295-315.

16. Harding K, Galano J, Martin J, Huntington L, Schellenbach CJ. Healthy Families America effectiveness: a comprehensive review of outcomes. *J Prev Interv Community.* 2007;34(1-2):149-179.

17. Williams, et al. *Healthy Families Florida Evaluation Report: January 1, 1999–December 31, 2003.* Williams, Stern, and Associates; 2005.

18. Frazier ER, Liu GC, Dauk KL. Creating a safe place for pediatric care: a no hit zone. *Hosp Pediatr.* 2014;4(4):247-250.

19. Saul J, Audage NC. *Preventing Child Sexual Abuse Within Youth-Serving Organizations: Getting Started on Policies and Procedures.* Centers for Disease Control and Prevention, National Center for Injury Prevention and Control; 2007.

20. Prinz RJ, Sanders MR, Shapiro CJ, Whitaker DJ, Lutzker JR. Addendum to "population-based prevention of child maltreatment: the US Triple P system population trial." *Prev Sci.* 2016;17(3):410-416.

21. Lanier P, Dunnigan A, Kohl PL. Impact of pathways Triple P on pediatric health-related quality of life in maltreated children. *J Dev Behav Pediatr.* 2018;39(9):701-708.

22. Roygardner D, Palusci VJ, Hughes KN. Advancing prevention zones: implementing community-based strategies to prevent child maltreatment and promote healthy families. *Int J Child Maltreat Res Pol Prac.* 2020;3:81-91.

23. Centers for Disease Control and Prevention. *Parent Training Programs: Insight for Practitioners.* Centers for Disease Control and Prevention; 2009.

24. Palusci VJ, Crum P, Bliss R, Bavolek SJ. Changes in parenting attitudes and knowledge among inmates and other at-risk populations after a family nurturing program. *Child Youth Serv Rev.* 2008;30(1):79-89.

25. Dubowitz H, Feigelman S, Lane W, Kim J. Pediatric primary care to help prevent child maltreatment: the Safe Environment for Every Kid (SEEK) model. *Pediatrics.* 2009;123(3):858-864.

26. Dubowitz H, Lane WG, Semiatin JN, Magder LS. The SEEK model of pediatric primary care: can child maltreatment be prevented in a low-risk population? *Acad Pediatr.* 2012;12(4):259-268.

27. McHugh MT, Kvernland A, Palusci VJ. An adolescent parents' programme to reduce child abuse. *Child Abuse Rev.* 2017;26(3):184-195.

28. Palusci VJ, Vandervort FE. Universal reporting laws and child maltreatment reports in large US counties. *Child Youth Serv Rev.* 2014;38:20-28.

29. Palusci VJ, Ondersma SJ. Services and recurrence after psychological maltreatment confirmed by child protective services. *Child Maltreat.* 2012;17:153-163.

30. Palusci VJ, Bliss R, Crum P. Outcomes after groups for children exposed to violence with behavior problems. *Trauma Loss.* 2007;7(1):27-38.

31. Palusci VJ, Covington TM. Child maltreatment deaths in the US National Child Death Review Case Reporting System. *Child Abuse Negl.* 2014;38(1):25-36.

32. Child Welfare Information Gateway. *Child Maltreatment Prevention: Past, Present, and Future.* US Department of Health and Human Services, Children's Bureau; 2011.

33. Helfer RE. The perinatal period, a window of opportunity for enhancing parent-infant communication: an approach to prevention. *Child Abuse Negl.* 1987;11(4):565-579.

34. MacLeod J, Nelson G. Programs for the promotion of family wellness and the prevention of child maltreatment: a meta-analytic review. *Child Abuse Negl.* 2000;24(9):1127-1149.

35. Alexander R, Baca L, Fox JA, et al. *New Hope for Preventing Child Abuse and Neglect in Maryland: Proven Solutions to Save Lives and Prevent Crime.* Fight Crime: Invest in Kids; 2003.

36. Chaffin M, Bonner BL, Hill RF. Family preservation and family support programs: child maltreatment outcomes across client risk levels and program types. *Child Abuse Negl.* 2001;25(11):1269-1289.

37. Commission to Eliminate Child Abuse and Neglect Fatalities. *Within Our Reach: A National Strategy to Eliminate Child Abuse and Neglect Fatalities.* Children's Bureau; 2016.

38. Klevens J, Barnett SBL, Florence C, Moore D. Exploring policies for the reduction of child physical abuse and neglect. *Child Abuse Negl.* 2015;40:1-11.

39. Klevens J, Luo F, Xu L, Peterson C, Latzman NE. Paid family leave's effect on hospital admissions for pediatric abusive head trauma. *Inj Prev.* 2016;22(6):442-445.

40. Jensen TK, Gulbrandsen W, Mossige S, Reichelt S, Tjersland OA. Reporting possible sexual abuse: a qualitative study on children's perspectives and the context for disclosure. *Child Abuse Negl.* 2005;29(12):1395-1413.

41. Walsh K, Zwi K, Woolfenden S, Shlonsky A. School-based education programmes for the prevention of child sexual abuse: a Cochrane systematic review and meta-analysis. *Res Soc Work Pract.* 2018;28(1):33-55.

PHOTOGRAPHIC ATLAS

Mary Case, MD

THE MEDICAL EXAMINER

The medical examiner plays multiple roles in the evaluation of a patient's injuries and death, especially in the injuries and death of a child. An appropriately trained forensic pathologist handles any sudden and unexpected death or any death suspected to be caused or contributed to by an injury or unnatural condition which is reported to the medicolegal authority that has jurisdiction where death was pronounced. The involvement of the medical examiner in child abuse and neglect cases traditionally begins at the time of death. However, when injured children are maintained in medical centers with supportive measures, the medical examiner may be notified and asked to become involved in the investigations long before death is pronounced. Further, with the advent of multidisciplinary child fatality review teams, the medical examiner may be part of community-wide efforts directed at preventing child injuries and deaths as well.

The following case studies describe the histories of the children and the results of the autopsies performed by a forensic pathologist. Each case includes detailed findings, photodocumentation of both internal and external injuries, and the determined manner and cause of death. The cases included in this chapter illustrate the types of injuries and cases that fall into the jurisdiction of the medical examiner or coroner.

Editor's note: The following case studies and corresponding photographs were provided courtesy of Dr. Mary Case.

FORENSIC AUTOPSY

Case Study 1[1]

This 3-year-old boy was found underwater in the bathtub according to his father. There were 2 previous accounts of abuse in the family with the father as the perpetrator: 1 account of physical abuse and 1 account of lack of supervision. The child was dead on arrival in the emergency department (ED). The cause of death was determined to be blunt abdominal trauma while the manner of death was determined to be homicide.

Table 1. Autopsy Results
FOUND AT THE SCENE
— Loop marks on the back, bruise near the left clavicle, bump on the forehead, and scars all over the body
— There was a skin graft visible, taken from the back of the right leg for the left foot
EXTERNAL EXAMINATION
— Old scar above the right brow
— Small petechial hemorrhages present in right inferior palpebral conjunctiva
— Several small petechiae present in both the upper and lower gingivae
— Skin graft noted above
— Right foot, old burn scar involving the entire dorsal surface *(continued)*

Table 1. Autopsy Results *(continued)*

EXTERNAL EXAMINATION *(continued)*

— Old scar on the midline of the lower back

— Old scar on the left lateral portion of mid-back

— Old scar on right hand

INJURIES

Type	Measurement
Fresh mucosal hemorrhage on the right buccal mucosa	2 mm x 4 mm
Healing scratch on left cheek	0.1 cm x 0.2 cm
Midline abrasion on abdomen above umbilicus	1.4 cm x 0.7 cm
Healing scratch on right shoulder	2 cm x 0.1 cm
Abrasion on right lateral neck covered with dried blood	1 cm
Abrasion on pinna of right ear	6 mm x 3 mm
Abrasion on the postauricular area	1.3 cm x 0.4 cm
3 purple contusions on right lateral chest	0.3 cm, 1.4 cm, 0.7 cm

INTERNAL EXAMINATION

Body Cavities

— Fresh subcutaneous hemorrhage seen on the chest underlying contusions

— Old adhesions on the right upper lobe of lung

— Fracture of the eighth rib laterally with callus and hemorrhage

Abdomen

Blood in the peritoneal cavity	240 mL
Laceration involving the spleen and adjacent soft tissue hemorrhage	6 cm x 2 cm
Laceration through the mesentery of the small bowel at the ligament of Treitz	4 cm
Hemorrhage through the tail of the pancreas	1 cm x 2 cm
Fresh hemorrhage in the lower midline abdominal wall	

Cranial Cavity

3 subgaleal hemorrhages	
— 1 old	2 cm
— 2 fresh	2 cm each

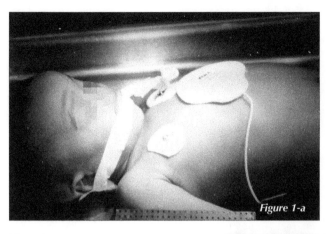

Figure 1-a

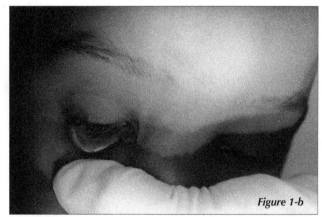

Figure 1-b

Figure 1-a. *Child before autopsy showing an old scar above the right brow.*

Figure 1-b. *Right inferior palpebral conjunctiva showing several small petechial hemorrhages.*

Figure 1-c. *Lower gingiva showing several small petechial hemorrhages.*

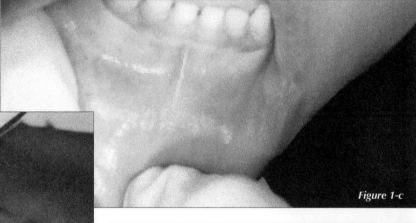

Figure 1-c

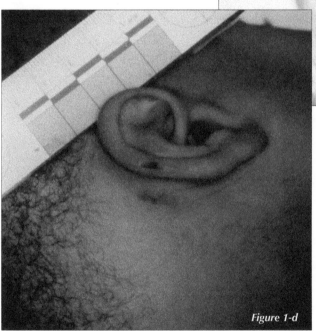

Figure 1-d

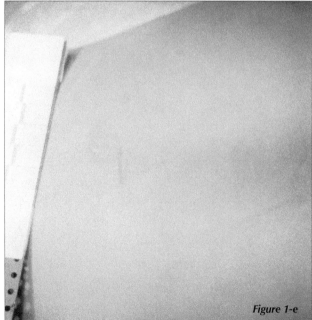

Figure 1-e

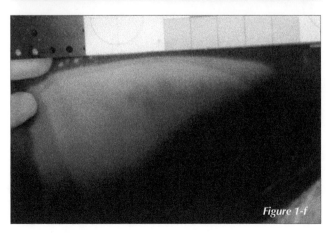

Figure 1-f

Figure 1-d. *Abrasion on pinna of right ear.*

Figure 1-e. *Lower back showing old scar.*

Figure 1-f. *Old scar on left lower back.*

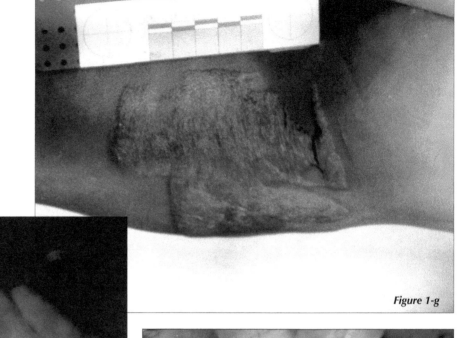

Figure 1-g

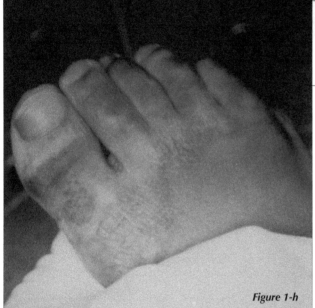

Figure 1-h

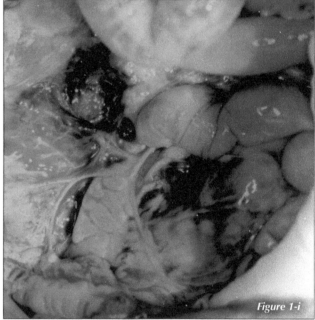

Figure 1-i

Figure 1-g. *Skin graft site scar on posterior right thigh.*

Figure 1-h. *Right foot with old burn scar over the dorsal surface.*

Figure 1-i. *Abdomen opened to show hemorrhage in soft tissue adjacent to spleen.*

Figure 1-j. *Abdomen opened to show laceration of mesentery.*

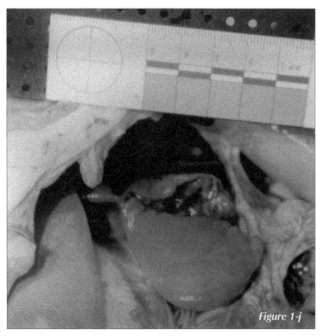

Figure 1-j

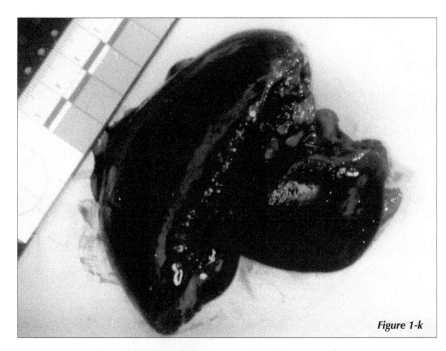

Figure 1-k

Figure 1-k. *Spleen removed to demonstrate laceration.*

Figure 1-l. *Chest opened showing hemorrhage over right eighth rib fracture.*

Figure 1-m. *Right eighth rib removed to show fracture.*

Figure 1-n. *Right eighth rib transected to show the fracture site.*

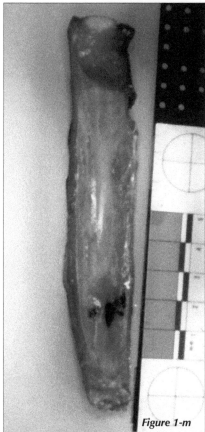

Figure 1-m

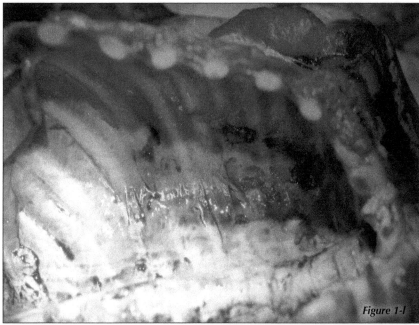

Figure 1-l

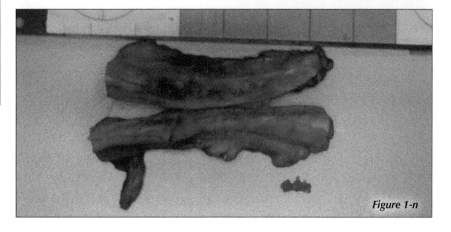

Figure 1-n

Case Study 2[2]

This 4-year-old girl lived with her mother and a male roommate. The mother was bipolar and schizophrenic and had been off her medications. On this day, the child was alone with the mother. The roommate returned to find the mother nude and wet while lying on top of the child, who was prone on the floor. The mother had her hand around the child's face, covering the mouth and nose, and was lying with her chest on top of the child's head. The mother was saying she did not want the dark angels to get her daughter and that she wanted her to go to Jesus. 911 was called, and the child was transported to the ED, where she was pronounced dead. This child suffered from cystic fibrosis that was diagnosed at birth. The cause of death was determined to be asphyxiation by suffocation and neck compression. The manner of death was determined to be homicide.

Table 2. Autopsy Results

EXTERNAL EXAMINATION

— The body was 48 inches and 51 pounds and normally developed

— Numerous petechial hemorrhages on skin of orbital regions bilaterally and extending onto the upper cheeks, greater on left than right

INJURIES

Type	Measurement
Red contusions, right upper cheek	43 mm x 20 mm
Red abrasion below left lower lid	5 mm x 2 mm
Purple contusion, bridge of nose	3 mm
Red contusion, left nasal ala	5 mm x 2 mm
Blue contusion, right lower lateral lip	10 mm x 5 mm
Red contusion, right lateral neck	10 mm x 5 mm
Red contusion, medial right arm	10 mm x 10 mm
Blue contusion and red contusion, posterior left arm	10 mm x 5 mm, 10 mm x 6 mm
Abrasions (4), left upper lateral chest	20 mm x 1 mm, 23 mm x 2 mm, 15 mm x 5 mm, 9 mm x 2 mm
Red contusion, left shoulder and adjacent axilla	45 mm x 20 mm
Blue-gray contusions (2), right lateral flank	10 mm x 1 mm, 20 mm x 1 mm
Red patterned area, right anterior leg	10 mm x 30 mm
Deep soft tissue hemorrhage in left lower back	15 mm

NEUROPATHOLOGY EXAMINATION

— Cranial cavity and brain were unremarkable

— BAPP staining negative for axonal injury

— Eyes negative for retinal hemorrhage

MICROSCOPIC EXAMINATION

— Lungs showed changes consistent with cystic fibrosis with bronchioles containing mucous and the bronchiolar walls containing mononuclear cells

— Pancreas showed marked abnormalities with dilatation of ducts that were filled with mucinous material, some of which was calcified; few islets; fibrosis of stroma

— Left lower back showed abundant hemorrhage in subcutaneous fat with neutrophils and mononuclear cells reacting

Table 2-b. Diagnoses

ASPHYXIATION BY SUFFOCATION AND NECK COMPRESSION

— Petechial hemorrhages, skin of right and left orbits and cheeks

— Contusions, right upper later cheek, bridge of nose, left nasal ala, right lower lip

— Abrasion, below left eye

— Contusion, right lateral neck

BLUNT TRAUMA

— Contusions (2), right medial arm, left posterior arm

— Abrasions (4), left upper lateral chest

— Reddish area of contusion, left upper lateral chest at shoulder

— Contusion, left lower back

HISTORY OF CYSTIC FIBROSIS

Figure 2-a. *Child at autopsy showing contusions of right cheek and contusions of right lateral flank.*

Figure 2-b. *Close-up of right orbit showing contusion on right cheek and petechial hemorrhages on skin of orbit and upper cheek.*

Figure 2-c. *Close-up of left orbit showing numerous petechial hemorrhages on skin of orbit and cheek.*

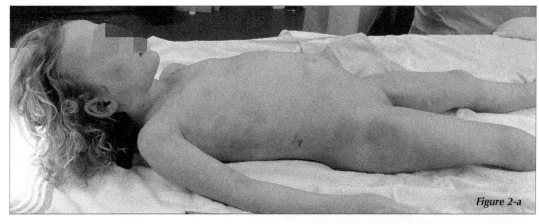

Figure 2-a

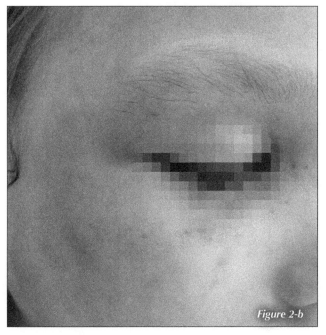

Figure 2-b

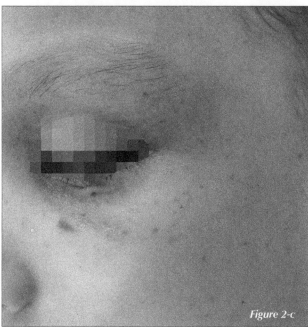

Figure 2-c

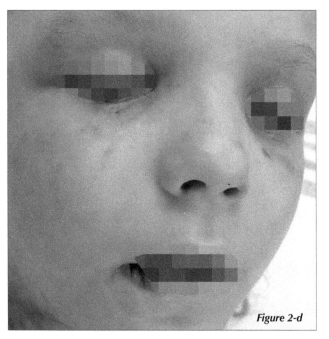

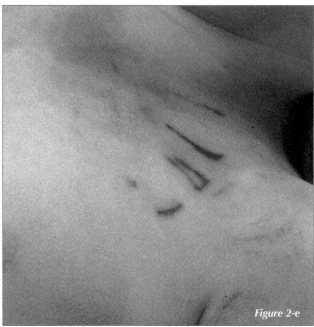

Figure 2-d. *Close-up of face showing contusion of bridge of nose, petechial hemorrhages of orbits and cheeks, and abrasion below left lower lid.*

Figure 2-e. *View of left upper chest. Neck showing 4 abrasions on left upper chest and contusion of left shoulder and adjacent axilla.*

Figure 2-f. *View of right side of neck and chest showing contusion of right lateral neck.*

Figure 2-g. *Close-up view of contusion of right lateral neck.*

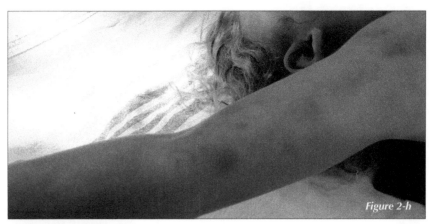

Figure 2-h

Figure 2-h. *Child at autopsy with contusion of right arm.*

Figure 2-i. *Right leg with patterned area on anterior surface.*

Figure 2-j. *Child at autopsy with contusion of left arm.*

Figure 2-k. *Child at autopsy with left flank showing 2 contusions.*

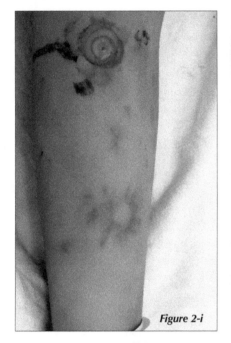

Figure 2-i

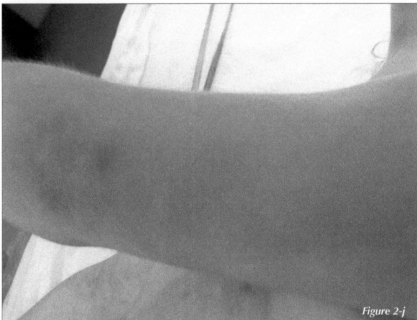

Figure 2-j

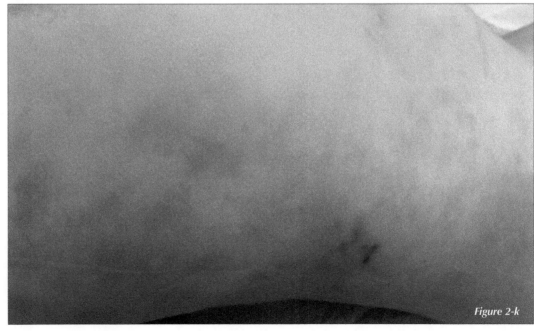

Figure 2-k

POLICE INVESTIGATION AND CHILD DEATH REVIEW TEAMS[3]

The role of the law enforcement in child maltreatment cases is first to determine if a crime has been committed and then to gather evidence regarding that crime. When a child is injured, law enforcement works closely with medical personnel and child protection workers to determine if the injury was deliberate, accidental, or the result of a natural disease process. In cases of suspected child abuse or neglect, the police investigator interviews potential suspects and witnesses, conducts scene examinations, and collects evidence for analysis. A thorough police investigation is as essential as a thorough home assessment or medical examination.

The most basic element of any child maltreatment investigation is the interview. Doctors, nurses, and ambulance personnel should be interviewed as soon as possible in order to get their version of the events while it is still fresh in their minds. Investigators usually interview individuals separately to avoid any cross-contamination. While detailed statements do require a significant amount of time, they are essential to ensure that any provided histories do not change over time.

Child maltreatment is one of the many fields that use interdisciplinary and multi-disciplinary teams and organizations. Such contacts are essential for the protection and advancement of children's safety; thus, it is important to be aware of other professionals who function outside of one's own discipline. Within the field of child maltreatment, there are many organizations that host conferences on local, national, and international levels. These organizations and conferences are invaluable learning resources for all members of the child death review team, which includes medical, social, and legal professionals as well as members of law enforcement. Additionally, various publications, including journals and books, assist in the dissemination of the most recent evidence-based research in the field of child maltreatment.

The following case studies include details regarding police investigations and the role of the various members of the multidisciplinary team while investigating a child's death. These cases include detailed histories and the evidence that assisted in the determination of the child's maltreatment.

TIMING

Case Study 3[4]

This 20-month-old girl died as a result of a massive infection from a torn bowel. Additionally, she had several facial bruises in different stages of healing. The biological mother said that the child had fallen while playing outside in a ground-level, homemade fort. The child had a small abrasion on the stomach that had apparently been caused by the fall. Immediately after the alleged fall, the child's condition rapidly deteriorated. She repeatedly vomited, could not walk properly, could not eat, and did not defecate or urinate. For 3 days, the mother stalled and refused to take the child to the hospital. She later explained to police that she feared that if the child went to the hospital, child protection workers would apprehend her because of the unexplained facial bruises. Eventually, the mother's relatives intervened and took the child to the hospital, but by that time, it was too late and the girl later died.

The medical examiner reported that it was highly unlikely that the fall would have resulted in the ruptured bowel and that the child's injuries were more consistent with a series of kicks or punches.

Figures 3-a and 3-b. *Note the facial and abdominal bruises.*

Figure 3-c. *At autopsy, numerous subgaleal bruises were found.*

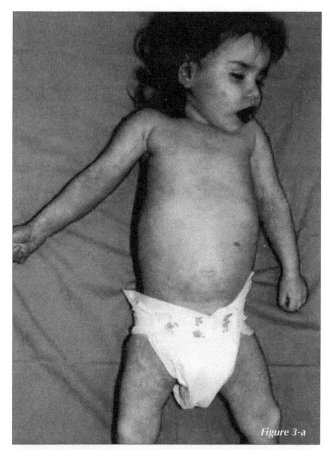

Figure 3-a

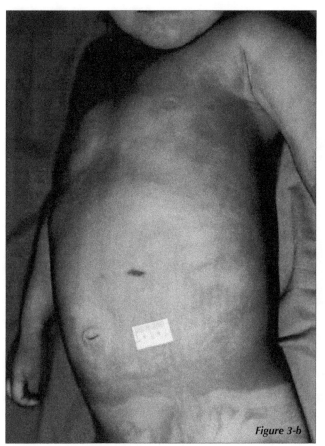

Figure 3-b

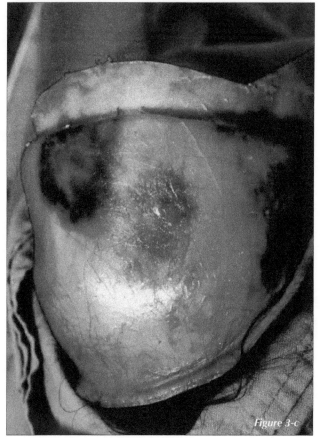

Figure 3-c

Long-Term Child Abuse

Case Study 4[5]

This 11-year-old physically and mentally disabled girl was living with her biological father and stepmother. The stepmother eventually killed the girl because she would not eat a meal. The father and stepmother then buried the girl underneath their trailer. Several months later, they unearthed the remains and took them with them when they moved to another state. Relatives of the girl eventually reported her missing, and police conducted investigations in both states. The father admitted to burying the child and then unearthing the body when they moved. Investigators used a backhoe to move the trailer back and then dug a trench beside the original burial site in order to preserve any evidence at the scene.

Figures 4-a and 4-b. *The original burial site is on the left of the photos.*

Figure 4-c. *Part of a plastic shunt found at the original burial site.*

Figure 4-d. *The child's skull from the storage site with the plastic shunt from the burial site re-inserted.*

Figure 4-e. *These are the 2 parts of the first cervical bone or atlas from the girl. The part on the left was found at the original burial site. The part on the right was found in a storage container with the majority of the child's skeleton in the new state where the father and stepmother had relocated.*

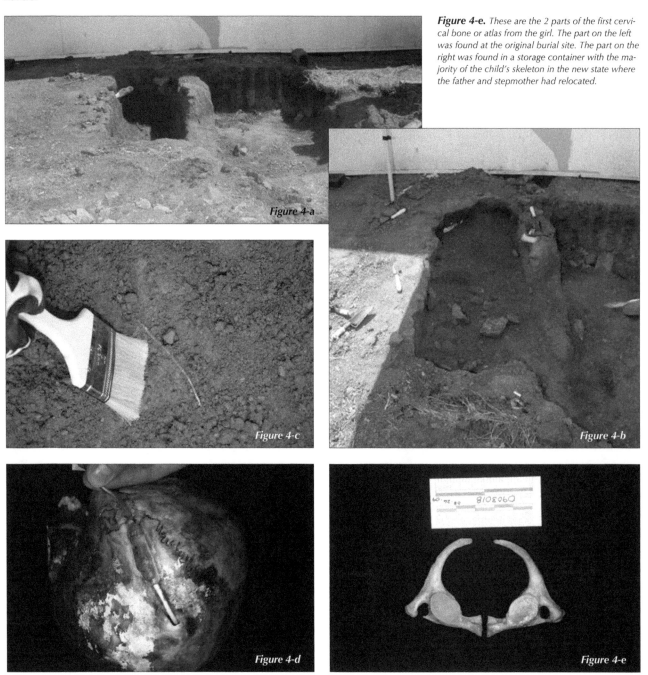

Figure 4-a

Figure 4-c

Figure 4-b

Figure 4-d

Figure 4-e

COURTROOM GUIDE[6]

Most child abuse cases do not involve courtrooms. However, both children and professionals may attend court when the case cannot be addressed through social service approaches alone. Courts in the United States operate on a federal and state level. Federal courts consist of district courts, the circuit courts of appeal, and the US Supreme Court. State court systems vary from state to state but typically include local courts with authority on specific issues and jurisdictions (eg, justice of the peace, police court, and probate court), county courts, and appellate courts. Courtrooms differ from location to location depending on the size of their jurisdiction and the types of cases they see (**Figures 5-a** through **5-d**).

Figure 5-a

Figure 5-b

Figure 5-a. *Lake City, Florida courthouse. A historic landmark.*

Figure 5-b. *Clearwater, Florida courthouse. Pinellas county.*

Figure 5-c. *Newton, Iowa courthouse. As is typical for many small town courthouses in the Midwest and Plains states, the courthouse sits in the middle of the town square and its purpose is instantly recognizable.*

Figure 5-d. *Tyler, Texas courthouse. Scene at dusk.*

Figure 5-c

Figure 5-d

COURTROOM ORGANIZATION[6]

Within the courtroom, the judge typically sits in the middle on a raised platform. The clerk sits to the judge's left and the witness to the right (**Figure 6-a**). Many courtrooms have a microphone for the witness for recording purposes and so that their voice may be heard. The 2 tables in the courtroom are for the defense and the prosecution (**Figure 6-b**). The position of the prosecution and defense varies depending on which side the jury occupies. The jury usually sits along 1 side of a courtroom (**Figure 6-c**). There are often 12 jurors in criminal courts within the United States, but the number can vary. Additionally, military courts have "panels" instead of "juries" and have some other procedural differences when compared to civilian courts.

Figure 6-a. *Interior of DuPage County courtroom. (Photograph courtesy of Jeff Kendall, JD.)*

Figure 6-b. *The prosecution sits on the right side of the defense and the left of this court. (Photograph courtesy of Jeff Kendall, JD.)*

Figure 6-c. *Jury location in this courtroom. (Photograph courtesy of Jeff Kendall, JD.)*

REFERENCES

1. Case ME, Kermgard EM. Abdominal trauma. In: Case ME, Kermgard EM, eds. *Forensic Pathology of Child Death: Autopsy Results & Diagnoses.* STM Learning, Inc; 2020:222-225.

2. Case ME, Kermgard EM. Subtle lethal abusive injury. In: Case ME, Kermgard EM, eds. *Forensic Pathology of Child Death: Autopsy Results & Diagnoses.* STM Learning, Inc; 2020:371-374.

3. Smith C. Police investigation atlas. In: Chadwick DL, Giardino AP, Alexander R, Thackeray J, Esernio-Jenssen D, eds. *Child Maltreatment: Cultures at Risk and Role of Professionals.* 4th ed. STM Learning, Inc.; 2014:673-694.

4. Smith C. Police investigation atlas. In: Chadwick DL, Giardino AP, Alexander R, Thackeray J, Esernio-Jenssen D, eds. *Child Maltreatment: Cultures at Risk and Role of Professionals.* 4th ed. STM Learning, Inc.; 2014:684.

5. Smith C. Police investigation atlas. In: Chadwick DL, Giardino AP, Alexander R, Thackeray J, Esernio-Jenssen D, eds. *Child Maltreatment: Cultures at Risk and Role of Professionals.* 4th ed. STM Learning, Inc.; 2014:693.

6. Alexander R. Resources and settings in the field of child maltreatment atlas. In: Chadwick DL, Giardino AP, Alexander R, Thackeray J, Esernio-Jenssen D, eds. *Child Maltreatment: Cultures at Risk and Role of Professionals.* 4th ed. STM Learning, Inc.; 2014:715-716.

TEST QUESTIONS

MULTIPLE CHOICE QUESTIONS

Select **1** correct answer for each question.

1. Which of the following are NOT rules of evidence as they apply to cases of child abuse and neglect?

    A. In response to efforts to introduce evidence, objections may be made by the opposing counsel

    B. The judge creates their own rules when determining the validity of evidence

    C. Circumstantial evidence, child witnesses, and hearsay testimony all pose evidentiary issues

    D. The use of admissible expert testimony and demonstrative evidence (eg, photographs) pose evidentiary issues

2. What level of prevention is used if an identified family experiencing intrafamilial violence is referred to their local resources?

    A. Primary

    B. Secondary

    C. Tertiary

    D. Quaternary

3. All of the following are reasons that children can easily become a target of child maltreatment without other individuals realizing EXCEPT?

    A. These crimes are often conducted in a private place, one-on-one, so there are no witnesses and no accomplices

    B. Children can sometimes be viewed as less credible or competent than the suspected adult offender

    C. Children often do not want the offender to be punished; they only want the abuse to stop, so they are hesitant to report

    D. Most crimes against children are isolated incidents

4. Nonaccidental physical injury, neglect, sexual abuse, and emotional abuse must be reported. Is this TRUE or FALSE?

    A. True

    B. False

5. Which of the following professional groups can play a role on CFR teams?

    A. Medical examiners

    B. Psychologists

    C. Educators

    D. All of the above

6. Which of the following are possible manners of death?

    A. Natural, intentional, suicide, undetermined

    B. Natural, homicide, accident, suicide, undetermined

    C. Natural, intentional, accident, suicide, undetermined

    D. Natural, homicide, accident, suicide

7. The child abuse reporting statutes designate who may take the child into custody, when they may do so, and under what circumstances. Is this TRUE or FALSE?

    A. True

    B. False

8. Which of the following are necessary steps of conducting an interview?

    A. Develop interview objectives prior to the start of the interview

    B. Establish the basis of the interview, including whether the suspect is or is not the person of interest and if they are free to leave the interview at any point

    C. Use a brief introduction and begin the building of a rapport with the interviewee based on the initial interview

    D. All the above

9. Which of the following is true of the advent of EBT?

    A. In the 1990s, most studies supported interventions from the behavioral and cognitive traditions

    B. EBTs are more commonly derived from the cognitive and behavioral fields

    C. In the 1990s, scientific focus shifted to identify techniques that yield greater outcomes than therapeutic rapport alone

    D. All the above

10. All of the following are considered a duty of law enforcement personnel when dealing with child abuse cases EXCEPT?

    A. Reporting and investigating crimes related to child abuse

    B. Communicating with adults and children involved in child abuse cases

    C. Conducting an autopsy in the case of death by suspected maltreatment

    D. Interviewing children, caregivers, and witnesses involved in child abuse cases

11. Families with housing and financial instability are associated with higher instances of fatal child maltreatment compared to nonfatally maltreated children. Is this TRUE or FALSE?

    A. True

    B. False

12. Which of the following procedures should be followed at a crime or event scene?

    A. Determine what crime/event has occurred

    B. Establish and protect the crime/event scene

    C. Process the scene

    D. All the above

13. Medical examiners do not participate in disease surveillance and/or collect vital information about societal issues such as emerging infectious diseases, suicides, and drug overdoses. Is this TRUE or FALSE?

    A. True

    B. False

14. Which of the following is LEAST important to discuss with the prosecutor in a court case?

    A. Reviewing the case in advance of testimony

    B. Fees

    C. Whether lunch will be provided or if it should be brought

    D. Location of testimony, where to park, and what time to appear

15. Which of the following questions is NOT useful when trying to establish rapport with a child?

    A. What is your name?

    B. Why is your caregiver hurting you?

    C. What school do you go to?

    D. How old are you?

16. Which of the following responsibilities falls to the medical examiner when the unexpected death of a child occurs?

    A. Identification and documentation of injuries or underlying illnesses/pathology

    B. Preservation of evidence

    C. Establishment of time of injury/injuries or death

    D. All the above

17. Which of the following is NOT true of the role of the state in child abuse cases?

    A. States abrogate privileged communications in a child abuse case

    B. Each state designates 1 or more agencies to receive reports of suspected child abuse and neglect

    C. All states have the same laws about reporting child abuse and neglect

    D. Each state has unique laws about reporting child abuse and neglect

18. Why are preliminary investigative checklists helpful?

    A. They help law enforcement structure their approach to the case

    B. They help remind law enforcement of what specific information to obtain

    C. They help organize and measure the status of an investigation

    D. All the above

19. All of the following is true of state reporting statute provisions EXCEPT?

    A. Provisions often make mandated reporters who fail to report suspected child abuse pay a fine

    B. Provisions often make it a criminal offense for mandated reporters to knowingly fail to report suspected child abuse

    C. Provisions often completely insulate reporters of abuse from a lawsuit

    D. Provisions often allow judicial interpretations of language, affecting whether related evidence is deemed admissible in court or not

20. Which of the following is true of child maltreatment fatalities?

    A. In the United States, an estimated 1770 children per year die from maltreatment

    B. Child maltreatment deaths have decreased in the past 20 years

    C. Most child maltreatment fatalities occur in children older than 3 years of age

    D. Most child maltreatment fatalities are not caused by neglect alone

21. What is the definition of prevention in the context of child maltreatment?

    A. The methods used after instances of child maltreatment have occurred

    B. The methods by which there is an attempt to lower the rates of child maltreatment

    C. The methods by which there is an attempt to raise the rates of child maltreatment

    D. The methods used to maintain child maltreatment rates

22. All of the following statements are true when giving testimony EXCEPT?

    A. If a lawyer asks if you agree with a reference, the correct response would be to state that you either wholly agree or wholly disagree with the given reference; it is important to state that references are typically absolutely authoritative

    B. If a lawyer rephrases the expert's testimony to enhance its presentation to the jury and/or judge, the correct response would be to listen carefully to the edited version and make certain that it is an accurate rephrasing, and if necessary, correct it if it is not

    C. If a lawyer implies that your opinions are based on speculation or guesswork, the correct response would be to state that your opinion is based on reasonable medical certainty, not speculation or guesswork

    D. If a lawyer asserts that child abuse is a legal determination, not a medical one, the correct response would be to state that child abuse is a medical diagnosis as well and that the legal and medical systems may not always agree

23. Which of the following statements regarding legal and medical environments are true?

    A. Medical professionals seek to diagnose and treat patient problems

    B. Lawyers seek to discredit the opposing side in each case

    C. Judges seek to ensure that cases will be upheld under the scrutiny of the court of appeals

    D. All the above

24. Civil actions cannot be brought against health care professionals or others based on their conduct in connection with a child abuse or neglect case. Is this TRUE or FALSE?

    A. True

    B. False

25. Which of the following statements is NOT true about the role of CPS?

    A. CPS is responsible for prosecuting perpetrators of child abuse and neglect

    B. CPS predominately implements treatment programs and intervention strategies for abused children and their families

    C. CPS assesses families' social service needs

    D. CPS predominately investigates abuse and neglect

26. All of the following activities have been supported by CFR teams EXCEPT?

    A. "Safe Sleep" programs promoting SIDS prevention and safe sleep environments for infants

    B. Quality assurance programs for medical examiner determinations

    C. "Safe Haven" laws to prevent newborn deaths

    D. Fire safety programs designed to increase smoke detector use

27. Why are EBTs not more widely utilized?

    A. Training in EBTs rarely occurs during graduate school training

    B. Training in a specific EBT can be costly and time consuming

    C. Some clinicians prefer to practice based on theoretical perspective

    D. All the above

28. Which of the following statements is NOT true about court cases?

    A. Juvenile court cases are typically heard by a judge

    B. Jury members are selected based on their knowledge of child abuse

    C. Criminal cases are heard by judges or juries

    D. A primary goal of court procedures is to ensure the rights of individuals

29. State law provides the authority for CPS home visits, either expressly or through implication, but, if individuals refuse to cooperate, a warrant or court order may be needed to gain access to a home. Is this TRUE or FALSE?

    A. True

    B. False

30. Which of the following are elements of successful prevention programs?

    A. A method for training program staff on how to best deliver the program model under a supervisory system

    B. A recommended duration, dosage, and clear guidelines for all those enrolled in programs

    C. A strategy for guiding program staff through balancing the delivery of program content with a family's cultural beliefs and immediate circumstances

    D. All the above

31. All of the following groups are tasked with implementing child maltreatment prevention programs EXCEPT?

    A. Attorneys

    B. Community members

    C. Various government agencies

    D. Health care providers/hospitals and health care offices

32. Cross examination tactics include: hostility, nicety, inconsistencies, two-in-one questions/statements, and attacks on one's competence. Which of the following techniques helps to mitigate these tactics and keep the testimony on track?

    A. Listening carefully to the question before answering

    B. Being aware of the various techniques being used

    C. Staying calm and avoiding an argument

    D. All the above

33. What level of prevention is used if children are being instructed on "good touch" and "bad touch" in school?

    A. Primary

    B. Secondary

    C. Tertiary

    D. Quaternary

34. Which statement is true of medical examiners and coroners?

    A. Medical examiners and coroners are both physicians, but a coroner is an elected or appointed official

    B. Medical examiners are physicians with specialized training while a coroner is an elected or appointed official who is not necessarily a physician

    C. Coroners are physicians with specialized training while a medical examiner is an elected or appointed official who is not necessarily a physician

    D. Both coroners and medical examiners are elected positions

35. Which of the following is a FALSE statement regarding the medical evaluation of an abused child?

    A. Only deem the diagnosis as "suspected abuse" because the medical professional does not know all the facts of the case

    B. A complete physical examination should be done and documented

    C. It is best to speak with the parents or caregivers individually, separate from the child

    D. All injuries should be photographically documented

36. Social services, police departments, health departments, and courts are all agencies who typically receive reports of suspected child abuse and neglect. Is this TRUE or FALSE?

    A. True

    B. False

37. Which of the following is NOT a possible indicator of SIDS death?

    A. Normal autopsy

    B. Unrevealing medical history

    C. Unrevealing inspection of the scene

    D. Bruising at the mouth and nose

38. The following are all true statements regarding the historical context of child mental health treatment EXCEPT?

    A. Contemporary approaches to mental health treatment are generally considered to have originated with Sigmund Freud

    B. Carl Rogers popularized the humanistic understanding of mental health as being largely a function of self-esteem

    C. Anna Freud gained widespread popularity for her work on phobias, namely treating "Little Peter" and his fear of rabbits.

    D. By the 1970s, academic psychology was undergoing significant changes with the advent of the cognitive revolution and the integration of scientific findings from research on higher order processes such as memory, problem-solving, and decision-making

39. All of the following are true about reporting incidents of child abuse or neglect EXCEPT?

    A. In some states, anyone who witnesses child abuse or neglect is considered a mandated reporter

    B. Educators, law enforcement, and health care workers are all mandated reporters

    C. In all states, anyone who witnesses child abuse or neglect is considered a mandated reporter

    D. Anyone can make a report to the state's child abuse and neglect hotline

40. Regarding CDR teams, which of the following is NOT an element of a trauma-informed approach to child death investigations?

    A. Approaching possible suspects with suspicion

    B. Approaching all interactions with surviving caregivers and family members nonjudgmentally

    C. Maintaining a bias-free investigation

    D. Navigating the tense environment of a death scene with care and regard for emotional distress of witnesses

41. Why are EBTs occasionally disputed within the child mental health field?

    A. EBTs are readily accessible for maltreated children

    B. Agencies must have multiple interventions available onsite to provide complete treatment for maltreated children

    C. EBTs require minimal training for clinicians

    D. There is a single intervention that can treat a multitude of presenting concerns that may occur after child maltreatment

42. The primary aim of a child abuse investigation is to determine who is at fault. Is this TRUE or FALSE?

    A. True

    B. False

43. Which of the following interventions is not generally considered to be an EBT according to most systematic reviews and guidelines?

    A. Dialectical Behavior Therapy

    B. Trauma-Focused Cognitive Behavioral Therapy

    C. Parent-Child Interaction Therapy

    D. Non-Directive/Child-Centered Play Therapy

44. What level of prevention is used if a local church opens an after-school resource for teen parents, offering them a safe place to go after school?

    A. Primary

    B. Secondary

    C. Tertiary

    D. Quaternary

45. Josie is a 17-year-old adolescent who is 32 weeks pregnant. Her 17-year-old boyfriend is the father of the baby, but they are not married. She lives at home with her parents who are supportive, and she has been receiving prenatal care at a local public health clinic. Which of the following would you NOT recommend in this scenario?

    A. Child Protective Services

    B. Nurse home visiting

    C. Triple P Parenting Program

    D. Family Nurturing Program

46. What should be done by medical professionals in order to prepare a case for court?

    A. Review any textbooks, journal articles, or other references that would assist in giving testimony

    B. Send a CV in case credentials are needed

    C. Review any deposition given previously

    D. All the above

ANSWER KEY

MULTIPLE CHOICE QUESTIONS

1. B	17. C	33. A
2. C	18. D	34. B
3. D	19. C	35. A
4. A	20. A	36. A
5. D	21. B	37. D
6. B	22. A	38. C
7. A	23. D	39. C
8. D	24. B	40. A
9. D	25. A	41. B
10. C	26. B	42. B
11. A	27. D	43. D
12. D	28. B	44. B
13. B	29. A	45. A
14. C	30. D	46. D
15. B	31. A	
16. D	32. D	

STM Learning, Inc.

Leading Publisher of Scientific, Technical, and Medical Educational Resources

www.stmlearning.com

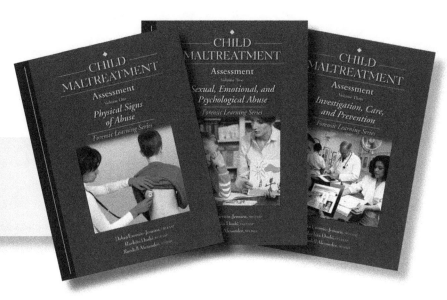

Helping professionals identify, interpret, and report child abuse

Table of Contents

Child Maltreatment Assessment
Forensic Learning Series

Debra Esernio-Jenssen, MD, FAAP; Ruchita Doshi, DO, FAAP; Randell Alexander, MD, PhD
366 pages, 469 images, 25 contributors total

Child Maltreatment Assessment, Bundle SPECIAL . . . . $240.00 *Print*
  ISBN 978-1-936590-89-6. . . $195.00 *eBook*
Child Maltreatment Assessment: Volume One ISBN 978-1-878060-31-0 . . $85.00 *Print*
  ISBN 978-1-953119-09-4. . . $70.00 *eBook*
Child Maltreatment Assessment: Volume Two   ISBN 978-1-878060-33-4 . . $85.00 *Print*
  ISBN 978-1-953119-10-0. . . $70.00 *eBook*
Child Maltreatment Assessment: Volume Three   ISBN 978-1-878060-35-8 . . $85.00 *Print*
  ISBN 978-1-953119-11-7. . . $70.00 *eBook*

The *Child Maltreatment Assessment* 3-volume set seeks to provide professionals from a variety of disciplines with the most comprehensive curriculum available for the diagnosis, treatment, and prevention of child maltreatment. Both novice and experienced members of the medical, social work, legal, law enforcement, and education fields will benefit from the vital information in these assessments. Each workbook also features a test section for readers to apply the knowledge they have gained, making this series ideal for group trainings or self-assessment.

These 3 workbooks cover the following areas:

— *Physical Signs of Abuse* helps readers identify common injuries found in maltreated children and learn how to distinguish abusive injuries from nonabusive injuries.

— *Sexual, Emotional, and Psychological Abuse* enables readers to identify sexual abuse, delineates which children are at high risk for abuse and neglect, and addresses the psychological sequelae of abuse.

— *Investigation, Care, and Prevention* outlines the recommended steps to take when abuse or neglect is discovered, details the agencies and procedures involved, and helps participants develop strategies for preventing abuse.

The photographic atlases contain additional high-quality images with accompanying case histories.

Orders are billed for postage, handling, and state sales tax, where appropriate.
Prices subject to change without notice.

STM Learning, Inc.

1220 Paddock Drive · Saint Louis, Missouri 63033
Phone: 314-434-2424 · Fax: 314-942-6486
www.stmlearning.com · orders@stmlearning.com

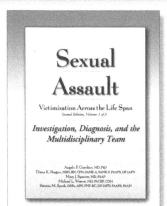

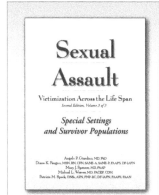

Educational Products for
Health Care Providers & First Responders

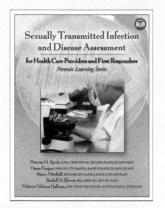

Sexually Transmitted Infection and Disease Assessment is a self-directed assessment featuring an anatomical review, an overview of 19 STIs and their symptoms, and detailed testing and treatment guidelines. Case studies covering the evaluation of both children and adults prepare readers to complete an assessment designed to refine their skills in diagnosis and follow-up care.

Patricia M. Speck, Diana K. Faugno, Stacey A. Mitchell, Rachell A. Ekroos, & Melanie Gibbons Hallman
260 pages, 144 images, 32 contributors

Sexually Transmitted Infection and Disease Assessment	ISBN 978-1-936590-85-8	. . . . $95.00 Print
	ISBN 978-1-936590-86-5	. . . . $80.00 eBook

Adolescent and Adult Sexual Assault Assessment (Second Edition) challenges forensic examiners to refine and apply their skills in sexual assault evaluation. Peer-reviewed case studies demonstrate identification and treatment techniques. Readers have the opportunity to assess themselves on 15 sexual assault case histories with accompanying examination photographs.

Diana K. Faugno, Stacey A. Mitchell, Trinity Ingram-Jones, & Patricia M. Speck • 166 pages, 90 images, 15 contributors

Adolescent and Adult Sexual Assault Assessment	ISBN 978-1-936590-78-0	. . . . $75.00 Print
	ISBN 978-1-936590-79-7	. . . . $65.00 eBook

Child Sexual Abuse Assessment guides forensic examiners through the process of identification and care in sexual abuse cases from infancy to adolescence. Readers will have the opportunity to assess 16 case histories of child sexual abuse with detailed accounts of each case and examination photographs for reference.

Patricia M. Speck, Diana K. Faugno, Angelia C. Trujillo, Tracey L. Wiese, Christine Hallas, Colleen O. James, & Jennifer L. Johnson • 200 pages, 153 images, 7 contributors

Child Sexual Abuse Assessment	ISBN 978-1-936590-19-3	. . . . $75.00 Print
	ISBN 978-1-936590-80-3	. . . . $65.00 eBook

Domestic Violence and Nonfatal Strangulation Assessment provides detailed, domestic violence-based case studies that describe the basics of evaluating strangulation patients. Readers are taught to identify symptoms, collect evidence, photographically document injuries, and treat strangulation victims.

Diana K. Faugno, Valerie Sievers, Michelle Shores, Bill Smock, & Patricia M. Speck
218 pages, 201 images, 12 contributors

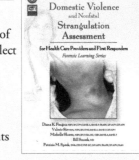

Manual Nonfatal Strangulation Assessment teaches novice first responders, SANE/SAFE practitioners, medical residents, and nursing students evidence-based evaluative methods of care for strangulation patients. The peer-reviewed c ontent enhances readers' continued competence in care of strangulation patients.

Diana K. Faugno, Angelia C. Trujillo, Barbra A. Bachmeier, & Patricia M. Speck • 138 pages, 112 images, 19 contributors

Domestic Violence and Non-fatal Strangulation Assessment	ISBN 978-1-936590-83-4	. . . . $95.00 Print
	ISBN 978-1-936590-84-1	. . . . $80.00 eBook
Manual Nonfatal Strangulation Assessment	ISBN 978-1-936590-70-4	. . . . $75.00 Print
	ISBN 978-1-936590-71-1	. . . . $65.00 eBook

Orders are billed for postage, handling, and state sales tax, where appropriate.
Prices subject to change without notice.

 **STM Learning**, Inc.

1220 Paddock Drive · Saint Louis, Missouri 63033
Phone: 314-434-2424 · Fax: 314-942-6486
www.stmlearning.com · orders@stmlearning.com

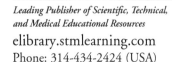

Printed in the USA
CPSIA information can be obtained
at www.ICGtesting.com
LVHW060018210923
758792LV00036B/391

9 781878 060358